HUMANS

How to Use Your SD-X Reader with This Book

This highly informative book introduces you and your child to humans—our past, our inventions, and our bodies—in a new interactive format. You can read the book and study the rich illustrations, but a touch of the SD-X Reader adds in-depth audio information, word definitions, and learning games to the pictures and text.

1. Press the Power button to turn the SD-X Reader on or off. The LED will light up when the SD-X Reader is on.

2. Touch the volume buttons found on this page or on the Table of Contents page in this book to adjust the volume.

3. Throughout the book, words in this color provide additional information when they're touched with the SD-X Reader. Objects on the page may also play additional audio.

4. At the top left corner of each spread, you'll see circles like these: ● ● Touch a circle to start a learning game or quiz. Touch the same circle again to stop playing the game. Touch another circle to start another learning game or quiz.

5. Some learning games will ask you to use Ⓣ Ⓕ buttons or Ⓐ Ⓑ buttons to answer. For other learning games, touch objects on the page to answer.

6. When you've answered all the questions in a learning game, you'll hear your score.

7. After two minutes of inactivity, the SD-X Reader will beep and go to sleep.

8. If the batteries are low, the SD-X Reader will beep twice and the LED will start blinking. Replace the batteries by following the instructions on the next page. The SD-X Reader uses two AAA batteries.

9. To use headphones or earbuds, plug them into the headphone jack on the bottom of the SD-X Reader.

CHANGE THE VOLUME WITH THESE BUTTONS:

UP   DOWN

Battery Information

Includes two replaceable AAA batteries (UM-4 or LRO3).

Battery Installation

1. Open battery door with small screwdriver.
2. Install new batteries according to +/- polarity. If batteries are not installed properly, the device will not function.
3. Replace battery door; secure with small screw.

Battery Safety

Batteries must be replaced by adults only. Properly dispose of used batteries. See battery manufacturer for disposal recommendations. Do not mix alkaline, standard (carbon-zinc), or rechargeable (nickel-cadmium) batteries. Do not mix old and new batteries. Only recommended batteries of the same or equivalent type should be used. Remove weakened or dead batteries. Never short-circuit the supply terminals. Non-rechargeable batteries are not to be recharged. Do not use rechargeable batteries. If batteries are swallowed, in the USA, promptly see a doctor and have the doctor phone 1-202-625-3333 collect. In other countries, have the doctor call your local poison control center. This product uses 2 AAA batteries (2 X 1.5V = 3.0 V). Use batteries of the same or equivalent type as recommended. The supply terminals are not to be short-circuited. Batteries should be changed when sounds mix, distort, or become otherwise unintelligible as batteries weaken. The electrostatic discharge may interfere with the sound module. If this occurs, please simply restart the sound module by pressing any key.

In Europe, the dustbin symbol indicates that batteries, rechargeable batteries, button cells, battery packs, and similar materials must not be discarded in household waste. Batteries containing hazardous substances are harmful to the environment and to health. Please help to protect the environment from health risks by telling your children to dispose of batteries properly and by taking batteries to local collection points. Batteries handled in this manner are safely recycled.

Warning: Changes or modifications to this unit not expressly approved by the party responsible for compliance could void the user's authority to operate the equipment.

NOTE: This equipment has been tested and found to comply with the limits for a Class B digital device, pursuant to Part 15 of the FCC Rules. These limits are designed to provide reasonable protection against harmful interference in a residential installation. This equipment generates, uses, and can radiate radio frequency energy and, if not installed and used in accordance with the instructions, may cause harmful interference to radio communications. However, there is no guarantee that interference will not occur in a particular installation. If this equipment does cause harmful interference to radio or television reception, which can be determined by turning the equipment off and on, the user is encouraged to try to correct the interference by one or more of the following measures: Reorient or relocate the receiving antenna. Increase the separation between the equipment and receiver. Connect the equipment into an outlet on a circuit different from that to which the receiver is connected. Consult the dealer or an experienced radio TV technician for help.

Cover image sources: iStock, PhotoDisc, ThinkStock

Product and sound element design, engineering, and reproduction are proprietary technologies of Publications International, Ltd.

Published by Louis Weber, C.E.O., Publications International, Ltd.
7373 North Cicero Avenue
Lincolnwood, Illinois 60712

Ground Floor, 59 Gloucester Place
London W1U 8JJ

Customer Service: 1-888-724-0144 or Customer_Service@pubint.com

www.pilbooks.com

 Publications International, Ltd.

Manufactured in China.

8 7 6 5 4 3 2 1

ISBN-10: 1-60553-908-2
ISBN-13: 978-1-60553-908-9

CONTENTS

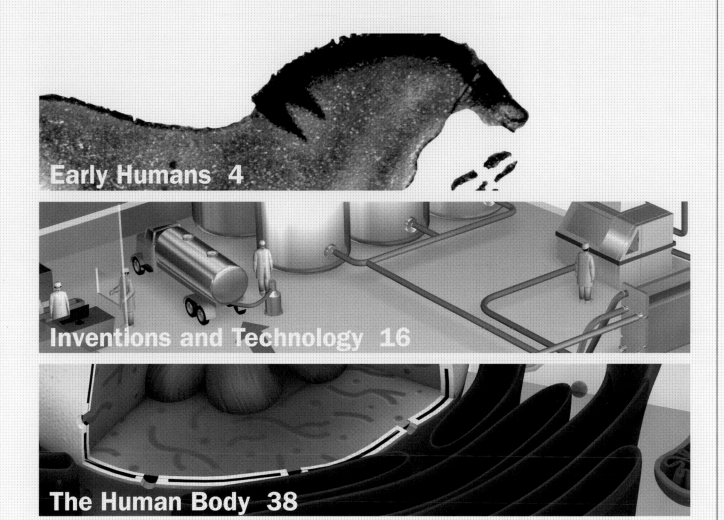

CHANGE THE VOLUME WITH THESE BUTTONS:

UP   DOWN

First Humans

The first humanlike creatures, *Australopithecus,* could walk in an upright posture with their hands free. It is believed that climatic changes, nutritional adaptations, and energy storage for movement contributed to *bipedalism*. Their short legs and long arms are seen as indications that they were only occasional walkers. Their brain was the size of a chimpanzee's.

LOCATION OF THE REMAINS OF THE FIRST HOMININS

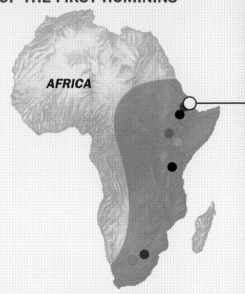

AFRICA

Adaptation to the Environment

Climatic changes probably transformed the tropical rainforest into savannah. Various species of *hominins* left their habitats in the trees and went down to the grasslands in search of food.

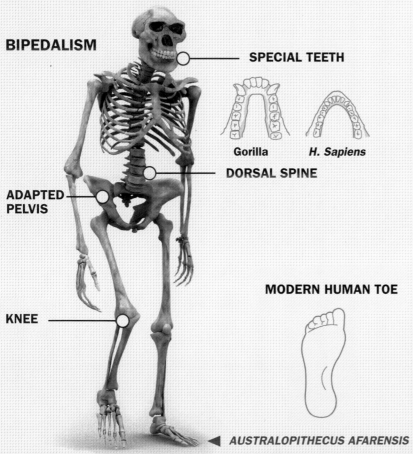

BIPEDALISM

SPECIAL TEETH

Gorilla   H. Sapiens

DORSAL SPINE

ADAPTED PELVIS

KNEE

MODERN HUMAN TOE

◄ *AUSTRALOPITHECUS AFARENSIS*

Archaeological Findings

The fossil skull of a child was found in 1924 in the Taung mine (South Africa).

SKULL OF TAUNG

2.5
MILLION YEARS AGO

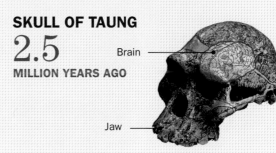

Brain

Jaw

FOSSILIZED FOOTPRINTS

3.6
MILLION YEARS AGO

4.4 MILLION YEARS AGO	4.2 TO 3.9 MILLION YEARS AGO	3 TO 2.5 MILLION YEARS AGO
Ardipithecus ramidus	*Australopithecus anamensis*	*Australopithecus africanus*

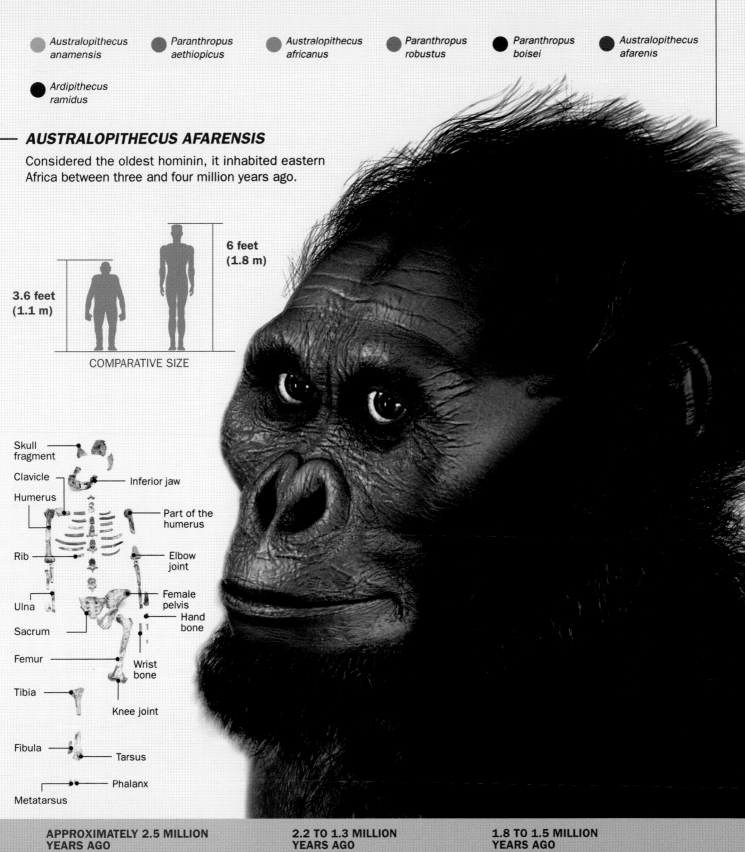

- Australopithecus anamensis
- Paranthropus aethiopicus
- Australopithecus africanus
- Paranthropus robustus
- Paranthropus boisei
- Australopithecus afarenis
- Ardipithecus ramidus

AUSTRALOPITHECUS AFARENSIS

Considered the oldest hominin, it inhabited eastern Africa between three and four million years ago.

6 feet (1.8 m)

3.6 feet (1.1 m)

COMPARATIVE SIZE

- Skull fragment
- Clavicle
- Inferior jaw
- Humerus
- Part of the humerus
- Rib
- Elbow joint
- Ulna
- Female pelvis
- Hand bone
- Sacrum
- Femur
- Wrist bone
- Tibia
- Knee joint
- Fibula
- Tarsus
- Phalanx
- Metatarsus

APPROXIMATELY 2.5 MILLION YEARS AGO	2.2 TO 1.3 MILLION YEARS AGO	1.8 TO 1.5 MILLION YEARS AGO
Paranthropus acthiopicus	Paranthropus boisei	Paranthropus robustus

Use of Tools

Homo habilis, which had a more humanlike appearance than *Australopithecus*, created various stone tools, such as flaked pebbles for cutting and scraping and even hand axes. The first signs of language appeared. *Homo erectus* migrated to areas far from its African origins, and it appears to have populated Europe and Asia, where it traveled as far as the Pacific Ocean. *Homo erectus* was capable of discovering fire.

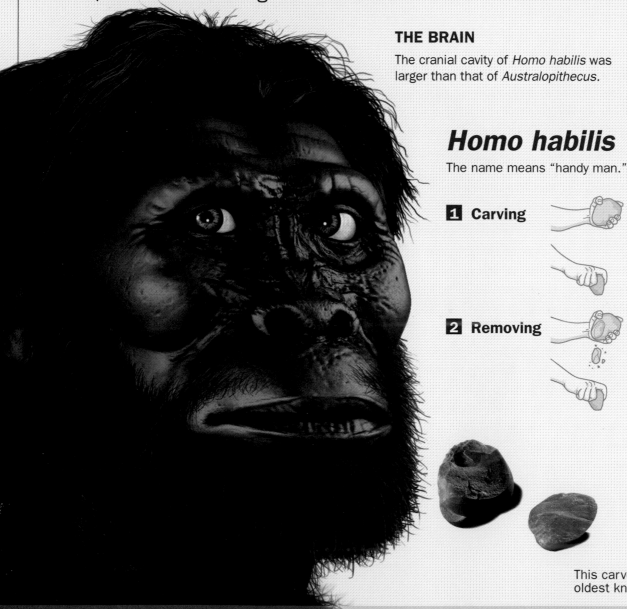

THE BRAIN

The cranial cavity of *Homo habilis* was larger than that of *Australopithecus*.

Homo habilis

The name means "handy man."

1 Carving

2 Removing

This carved rock is the oldest known tool.

2.5 MILLION YEARS AGO	1.7 MILLION YEARS AGO	1.6 MILLION YEARS AGO
Homo habilis appears.	*Homo erectus* leaves its habitat.	*Homo habilis* disappears.

ASIA

◼ Homo habilis **◼ Homo erectus**

AFRICA

Homo erectus

This species was tall and had long limbs.

**MAP OF LOCATIONS
AND MIGRATIONS**

ARCHAEOLOGICAL FINDINGS

**SKULL OF
*HOMO HABILIS***

**SKULL OF
*HOMO ERECTUS***

Hand axe in the
shape of a drop

FIRE

The first evidence of the use of fire
is some 1,500,000 years ago.

**ABOUT 1.5 MILLION
YEARS AGO**

First use of fire by
Homo erectus.

Able Hunters

Descendants of *Homo heidelbergensis*, the Neanderthals were the first inhabitants of Europe, western Asia, and northern Africa. According to fossil evidence, Neanderthals were the first humans to adapt to the extreme climate of the glacial era, to carry out funerals, and to care for sick individuals. The cause of their *extinction* is still under debate.

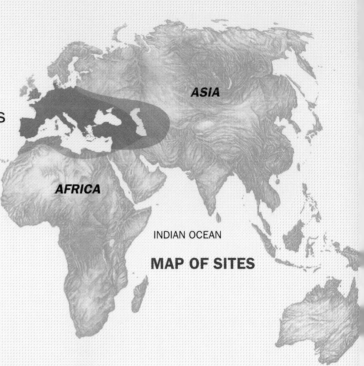

ASIA

AFRICA

INDIAN OCEAN

MAP OF SITES

Homo neanderthalensis

GRAVES

60,000 years ago

THE AGE OF SOME
NEANDERTHAL DISCOVERIES

MAN—HUNTER

SHELTERS

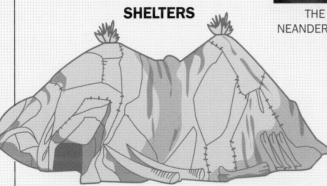

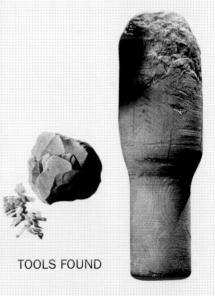

TOOLS FOUND

600,000 YEARS AGO	400,000 YEARS AGO	160,000 YEARS AGO
Homo heidelbergensis is in Europe, part of Asia, and Africa.	Wooden spears found in Germany and the United Kingdom date back to this time.	First *Homo sapiens* found in Africa

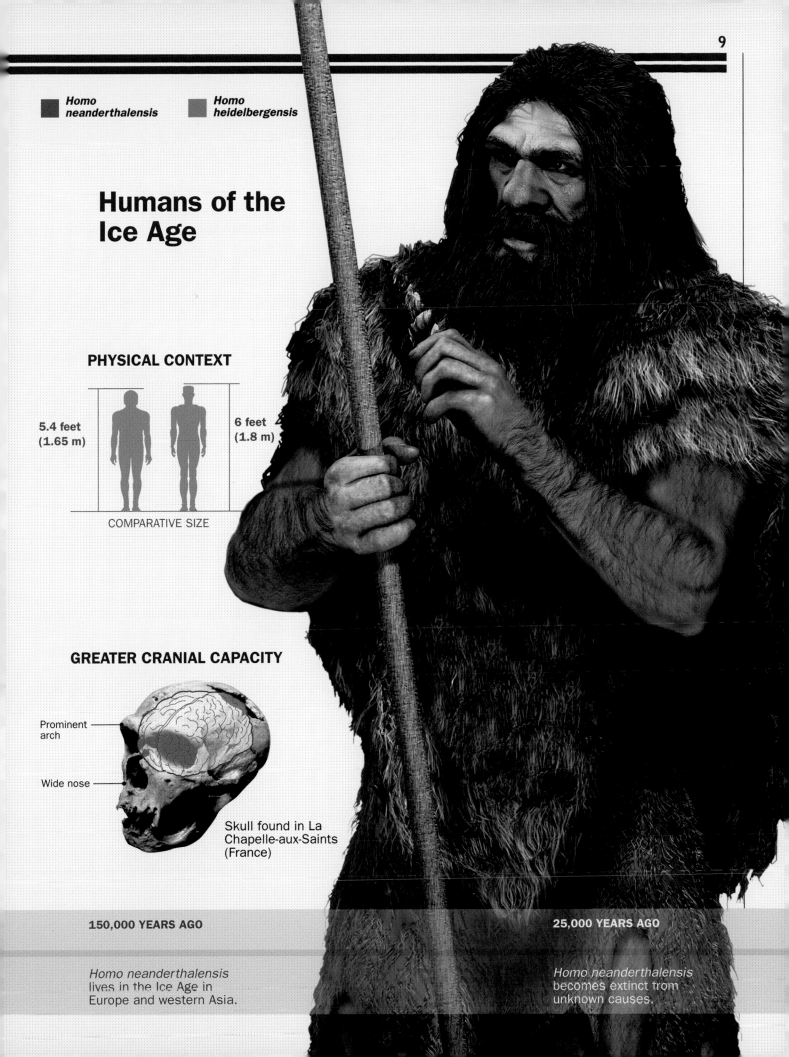

Homo
neanderthalensis

Homo
heidelbergensis

Humans of the Ice Age

PHYSICAL CONTEXT

5.4 feet
(1.65 m)

6 feet
(1.8 m)

COMPARATIVE SIZE

GREATER CRANIAL CAPACITY

Prominent arch

Wide nose

Skull found in La
Chapelle-aux-Saints
(France)

150,000 YEARS AGO

Homo neanderthalensis
lives in the Ice Age in
Europe and western Asia.

25,000 YEARS AGO

Homo neanderthalensis
becomes extinct from
unknown causes.

Direct Ancestors

The origin of the human species is still in debate, even though scientists have been able to establish that *H. sapiens* is not directly related to the Neanderthals. The most accepted scientific studies for dating Neanderthal fossils place the oldest specimens some 195,000 years ago in Africa. New genetic studies based on *mitochondrial DNA* have corroborated that date and have also contributed to determining the possible migration routes that permitted the slow expansion of H. sapiens to other continents.

Homo sapiens sapiens

It is believed that Cro-Magnon arrived in Europe some 40,000 years ago. Evidence of prehistoric art, symbolism, and ritual ceremonies distinguish this advanced culture from other species of hominins that preceded it.

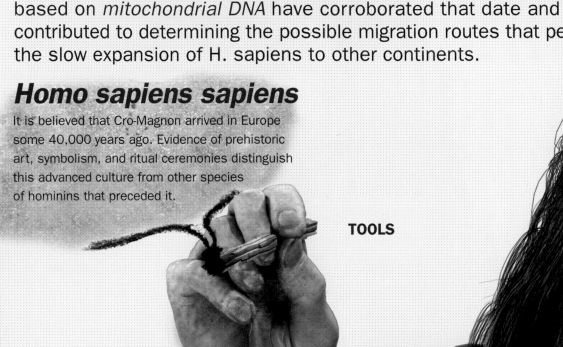

TOOLS

CRANIAL CAPACITY

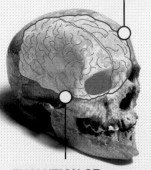

EVOLUTION OF THE SKULL

150,000 YEARS AGO

120,000 YEARS AGO

"Mitochondrial Eve"

Homo sapiens begins to extend through Africa.

Theories of Expansion

There is no agreement among scientists about how the expansion of *Homo sapiens* to the entire world took place. One theory is that the "Mitochondrial Eve," the most recent common ancestor, lived in Africa. From there, in migration waves, *Homo sapiens* would have reached Asia, Australia and Europe.

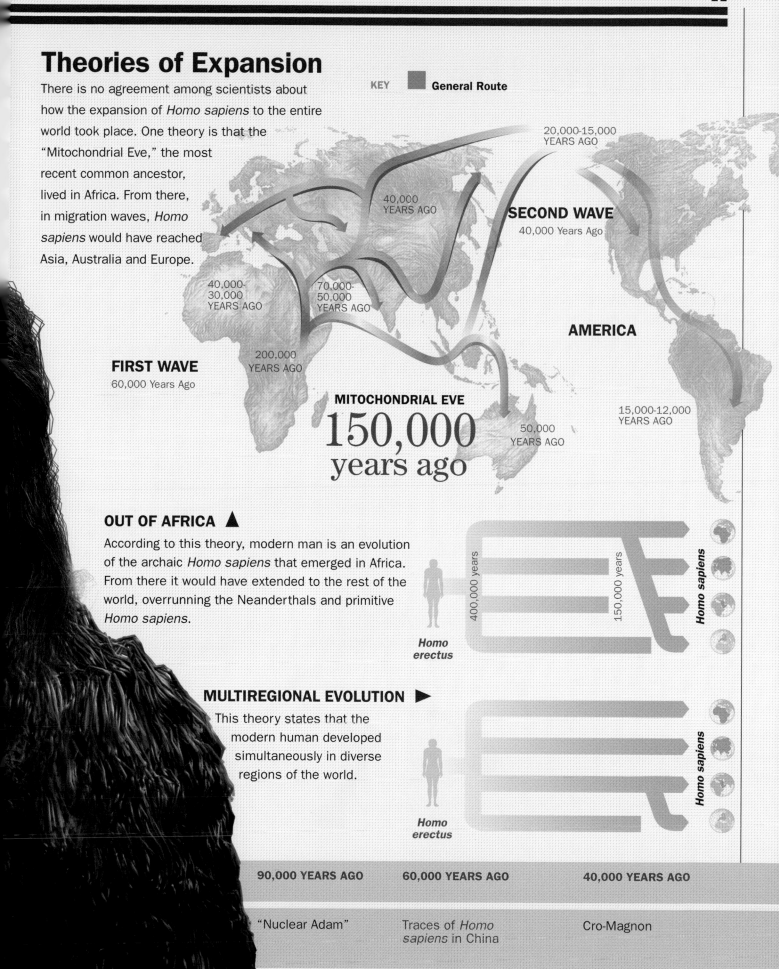

KEY   **General Route**

20,000-15,000
YEARS AGO

40,000
YEARS AGO

SECOND WAVE
40,000 Years Ago

40,000-
30,000
YEARS AGO

70,000-
50,000
YEARS AGO

200,000
YEARS AGO

FIRST WAVE
60,000 Years Ago

AMERICA

MITOCHONDRIAL EVE

150,000
years ago

50,000
YEARS AGO

15,000-12,000
YEARS AGO

OUT OF AFRICA ▲

According to this theory, modern man is an evolution of the archaic *Homo sapiens* that emerged in Africa. From there it would have extended to the rest of the world, overrunning the Neanderthals and primitive *Homo sapiens*.

400,000 years

Homo erectus

150,000 years

Homo sapiens

MULTIREGIONAL EVOLUTION ▶

This theory states that the modern human developed simultaneously in diverse regions of the world.

Homo erectus

Homo sapiens

90,000 YEARS AGO	60,000 YEARS AGO	40,000 YEARS AGO
"Nuclear Adam"	Traces of *Homo sapiens* in China	Cro-Magnon

Culture, the Great Leap

Although questions remain about how culture originated, it is almost impossible to determine which things of the human world are natural and which are not. Scientists of many disciplines are trying to answer these questions from the evidence of prehistoric life found by paleontologists. The first traces of agriculture, industry, population centers, and control over nature date from barely the last 10,000 years. Some believe that the definitive leap toward culture was achieved through the acquisition of a creative language capable of expressing ideas and sentiments more advanced than the simple communication of *Homo erectus*.

The First Artists

Cave paintings leave no doubt that those who made them truly possessed the attributes of human beings.

CAVE-PAINTING TECHNIQUES

GEOMETRIC DESIGNS

BLOWING

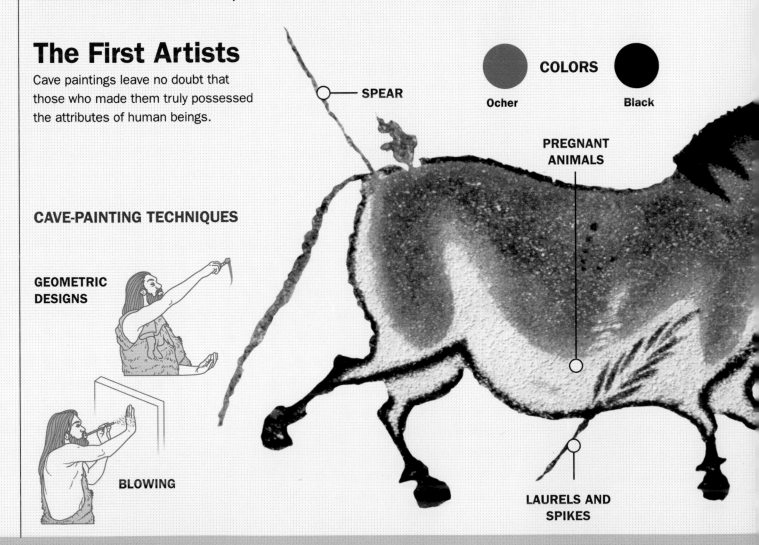

SPEAR

COLORS

Ocher

Black

PREGNANT ANIMALS

LAURELS AND SPIKES

WÜRM GLACIATION 35,000 YEARS AGO	AURIGNACIAN 30,000 YEARS AGO	PERIGORDIAN 27,000 YEARS AGO
The Upper Paleolithic begins.	Tools of mammoth tusk, flake tools	Well-cut tools, including a multi-angle graver

Art on the Walls

Cave painting is a phenomenon that was found mainly in the current regions of France and Spain. Portable art was abundant in all Europe.

● Sites in Europe where Paleolithic art has been found

EUROPE

Black Sea

Mediterranean Sea

The head is small in relation to the rest of the animal's body.

Builders of Objects

Homo sapiens sapiens distinguished itself from its ancestors, who were already making rudimentary tools, through the growing use of such new materials as bone and above all for the specialization of new tools.

THIS LITTLE STATUE IS

24,000
years old

OTHER THEMES AND MOTIVES

PALEOLITHIC TOOLS

TWO-SIDED KNIFE

POLISHED AX

HARPOON

SOLUTREAN 50,000-20,000 YEARS AGO

Use of oxide to paint, pointed instruments

MAGDALENIAN 15,000 YEARS AGO

The greatest flourishing of cave art in southern Europe

END OF PALEOLITHIC 9,000 BC

End of the glaciations, with an improvement of the global climate

Urban Revolution

Some 10,000 years ago, there was an interglacial period on Earth that caused a gradual increase in temperatures and an overall climatic change that brought a modification to the life of humans. Instead of roaming from place to place to hunt, people began to create societies based on *sedentary* life, agriculture, and the *domestication* of animals. Some villages grew so much that they became true cities, such as Çatal Hüyük in southern Turkey in 6000 BC.

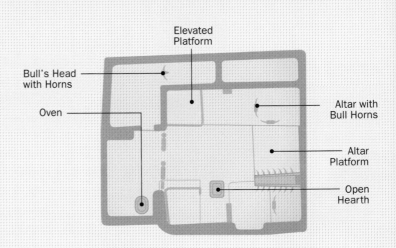

Elevated Platform
Bull's Head with Horns
Oven
Altar with Bull Horns
Altar Platform
Open Hearth

The Neolithic City of Çatal Hüyük

During the excavation, many religious articles were uncovered: the majority were ceramic figures in relief depicting the *mother goddess* and heads of bulls and leopards.

CROPS

Lentils   **Apples**   **Wheat**

270 square feet
(25 sq m)
WAS THE AVERAGE SIZE OF A HOUSE

CONSTRUCTION OF MEGALITHS

1 Transport   **2 Erection**   **3 Earthworks**   **4 Trilith**

8000 BC	7000 BC	6000 BC	3500 BC
First indications of agricultural activities	Expansion of agriculture. Complex *funerary* rites.	Stable settlements in the Persian Gulf	Invention of writing in Mesopotamia

Incredible Petra

Petra was founded in the 4th century BC by the Nabataeans, a nomadic people. The Nabataeans were merchants and raiders who became prosperous by controlling the spice trade. The city, carved in sandstone, knew times of splendor, but it eventually fell into ruin.

Temples and tombs

Original Walls

Christian Tombs

Treasury

Amphitheater

Habis Castle

Great Temple

Byzantine Walls

Main Street

HIDDEN IN THE DESERT

The Treasury

THIS BUILDING MAY HAVE HOUSED A PHARAOH'S TREASURE.

Uncertain Origins

Experts find it difficult to establish Petra's dates of construction.

THE GOD SERAPIS

CARVED IN STONE

2000 BC

First vehicles with spoked wheels in Asia

Olive Oil

Olive oil has been a part of people's diet since antiquity, and even today it is one of the most popular oils because of its flavor and nutritious properties. Obtaining high-quality olive oil involves a chain of processes that begins at the tree and ends with the packaging of the end product. The quality begins in the fields and depends on a combination of soil, climate, tree variety, and cultivation and harvesting techniques. The remaining operations in the extraction process (transportation, storage, manufacturing, and extraction of the oil) are responsible for maintaining that quality.

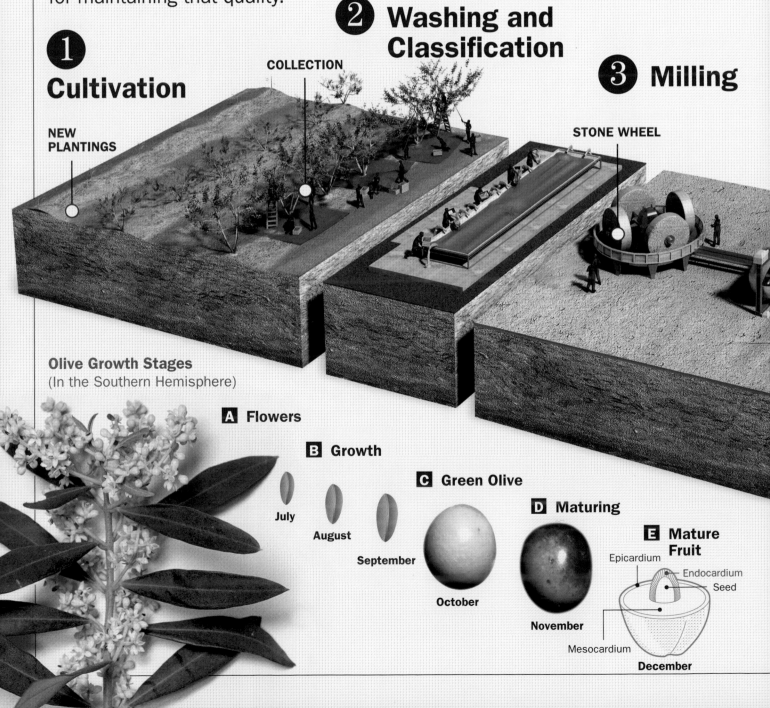

① Cultivation

NEW PLANTINGS

COLLECTION

② Washing and Classification

③ Milling

STONE WHEEL

Olive Growth Stages
(In the Southern Hemisphere)

A Flowers

B Growth

July

August

September

C Green Olive

October

D Maturing

November

E Mature Fruit

Epicardium

Endocardium

Seed

Mesocardium

December

22 pounds
(10 kg)

IS THE QUANTITY OF OLIVES NEEDED TO EXTRACT 0.5 GALLON (2 L) OF OIL.

THREE TYPES OF OIL

1. Virgin Olive Oil
2. Refined Olive Oil
3. Olive Oil

COMPOSITION OF AN OLIVE

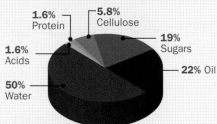

- **1.6%** Protein
- **5.8%** Cellulose
- **1.6%** Acids
- **19%** Sugars
- **22%** Oil
- **50%** Water

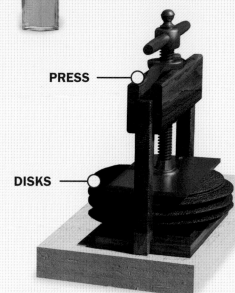

PRESS

DISKS

④ Pressing

FILTER

RESIDUE

STAINLESS STEEL HOPPER

⑤ Refining

HOMOGENIZING

⑥ Storage

BOTTLE

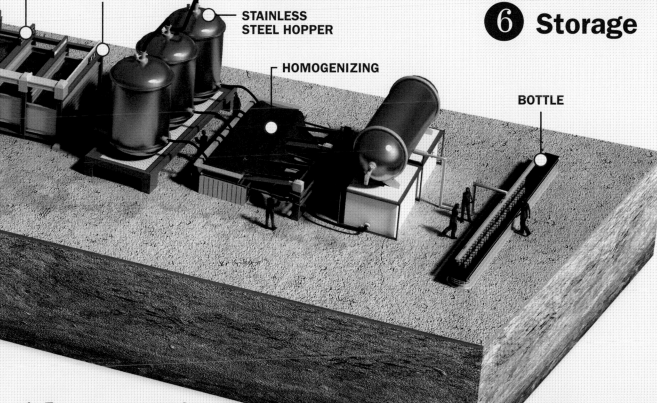

⑦ Bottling

Alternating Years
After a good crop, olive trees usually do not produce well the following year.

Tomato Factories

Tomato

The tomato, eaten in the Americas for a long time, is now consumed globally. Its cultivation has been changed by technological advances that help address problems of infestation and adverse environmental conditions. It is even possible to grow tomatoes without using soil.

Traditional Cultivation

Planting	End of Winter
Harvesting	Beginning of Summer

5.5 pounds
(2.5 kg)

THE AVERAGE WEIGHT OF TOMATOES A PLANT CAN PRODUCE IN ONE YEAR

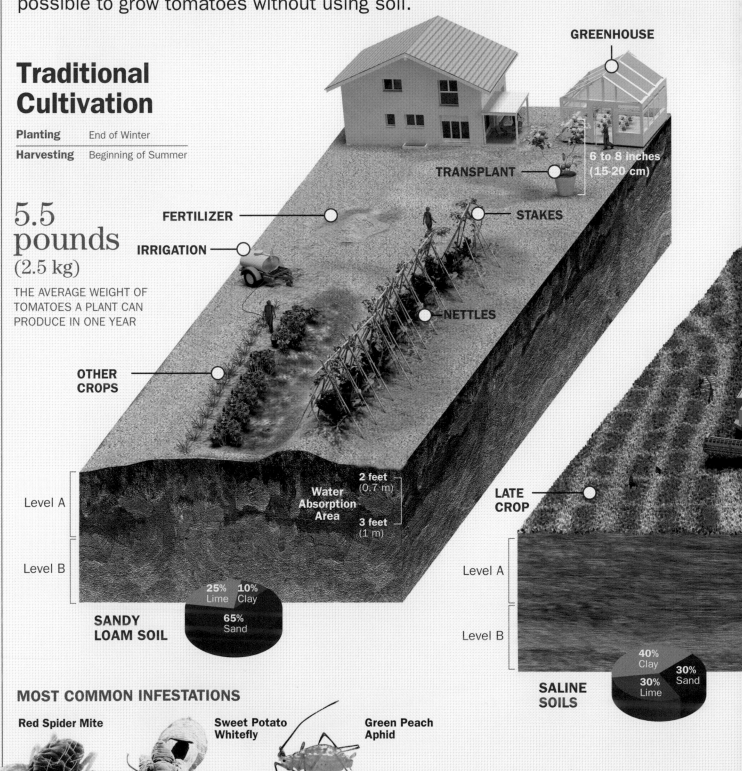

GREENHOUSE

TRANSPLANT

6 to 8 inches (15-20 cm)

FERTILIZER

IRRIGATION

STAKES

NETTLES

OTHER CROPS

Level A

Level B

Water Absorption Area

2 feet (0.7 m)

3 feet (1 m)

SANDY LOAM SOIL

25% Lime 10% Clay
65% Sand

LATE CROP

Level A

Level B

SALINE SOILS

40% Clay
30% Lime 30% Sand

MOST COMMON INFESTATIONS

Red Spider Mite

Sweet Potato Whitefly

Green Peach Aphid

Transgenic Crop

Planting   Winter

Harvesting   Summer/Autumn

ORIGIN OF THE TOMATO

● Area of Origin

○ Main Producers

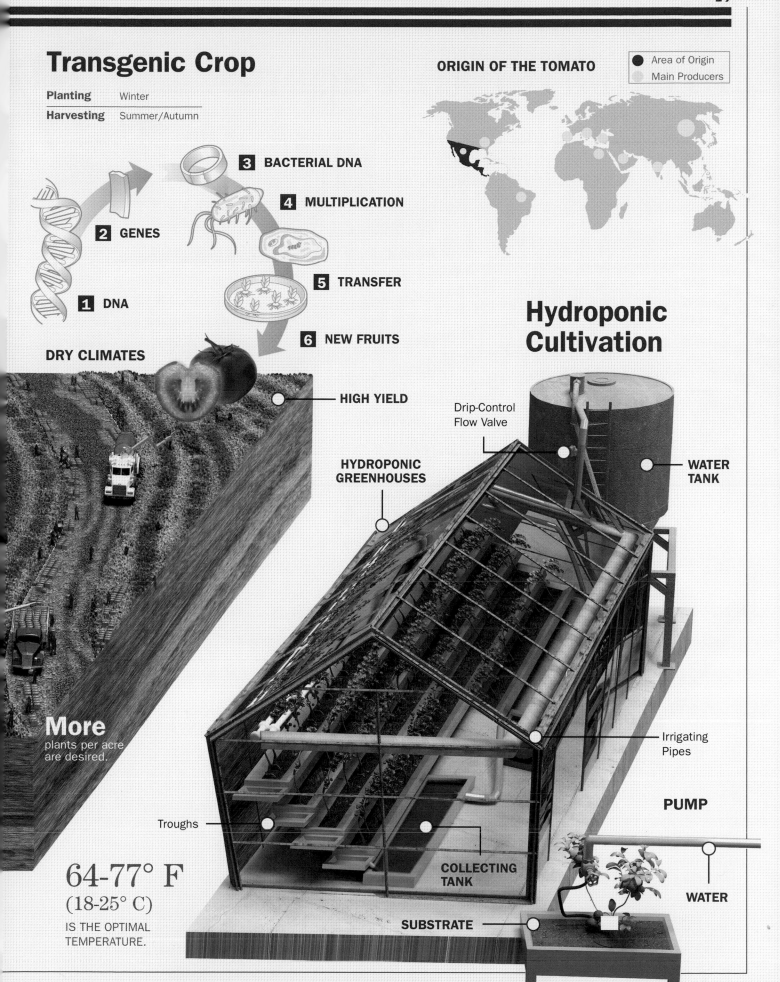

3 BACTERIAL DNA

4 MULTIPLICATION

2 GENES

5 TRANSFER

1 DNA

6 NEW FRUITS

DRY CLIMATES

HIGH YIELD

Hydroponic Cultivation

Drip-Control Flow Valve

HYDROPONIC GREENHOUSES

WATER TANK

Irrigating Pipes

More
plants per acre
are desired.

Troughs

PUMP

COLLECTING TANK

WATER

64-77° F
(18-25° C)

IS THE OPTIMAL
TEMPERATURE.

SUBSTRATE

From Tree to Paper

The basic process of manufacturing paper has not changed for 2,000 years, although technology today allows us to manufacture paper in quantities that are immeasurably greater than those of the papyrus produced in antiquity. Worldwide, one of the most commonly used trees for paper manufacture is the eucalyptus because of its quick growth, its capacity to resprout trees from the stumps of young trees, its wood's quality, its consistency, and its yield.

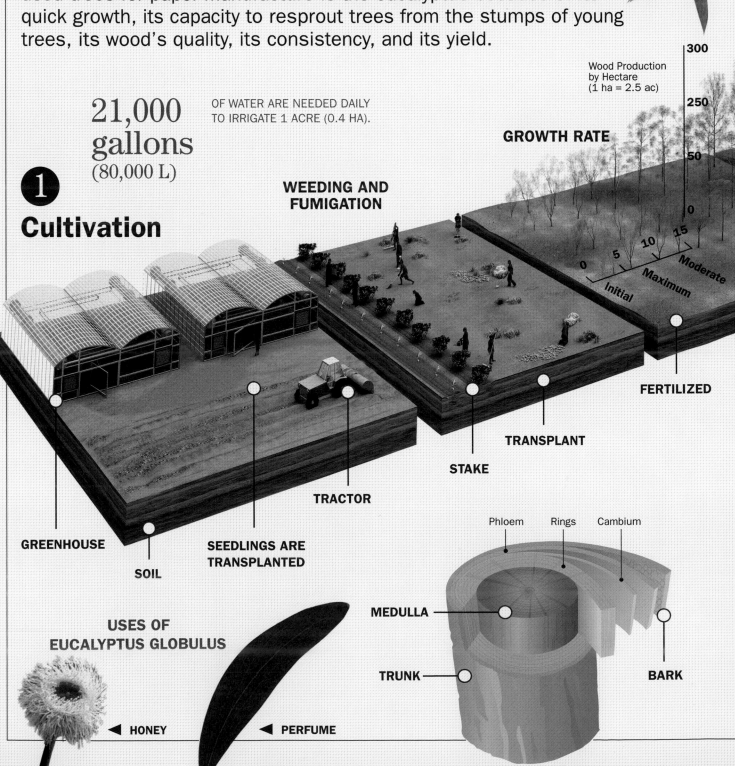

21,000 gallons
(80,000 L)

OF WATER ARE NEEDED DAILY TO IRRIGATE 1 ACRE (0.4 HA).

1 Cultivation

Wood Production by Hectare
(1 ha = 2.5 ac)

GROWTH RATE

300
250
50
0

Initial   Maximum   Moderate
0   5   10   15

WEEDING AND FUMIGATION

FERTILIZED

TRANSPLANT

STAKE

TRACTOR

GREENHOUSE

SEEDLINGS ARE TRANSPLANTED

SOIL

USES OF EUCALYPTUS GLOBULUS

◄ HONEY   ◄ PERFUME

Phloem   Rings   Cambium

MEDULLA

TRUNK

BARK

◀ **EUCALYPTUS**

② Clear-Cutting

10-13 years
IS THE OPTIMAL AGE
FOR CUTTING.

**CLEAR-CUTTING
MACHINE**

TRANSPORTATION

50 cubic
feet (15 cu m)
IS THE AMOUNT
OF WOOD PRODUCED
PER HECTARE.

③ Debarking, Washing, and Splintering

DEBARKER

WASHER

**CHIPPING
MACHINE**

④ Manufacture of the Pulp

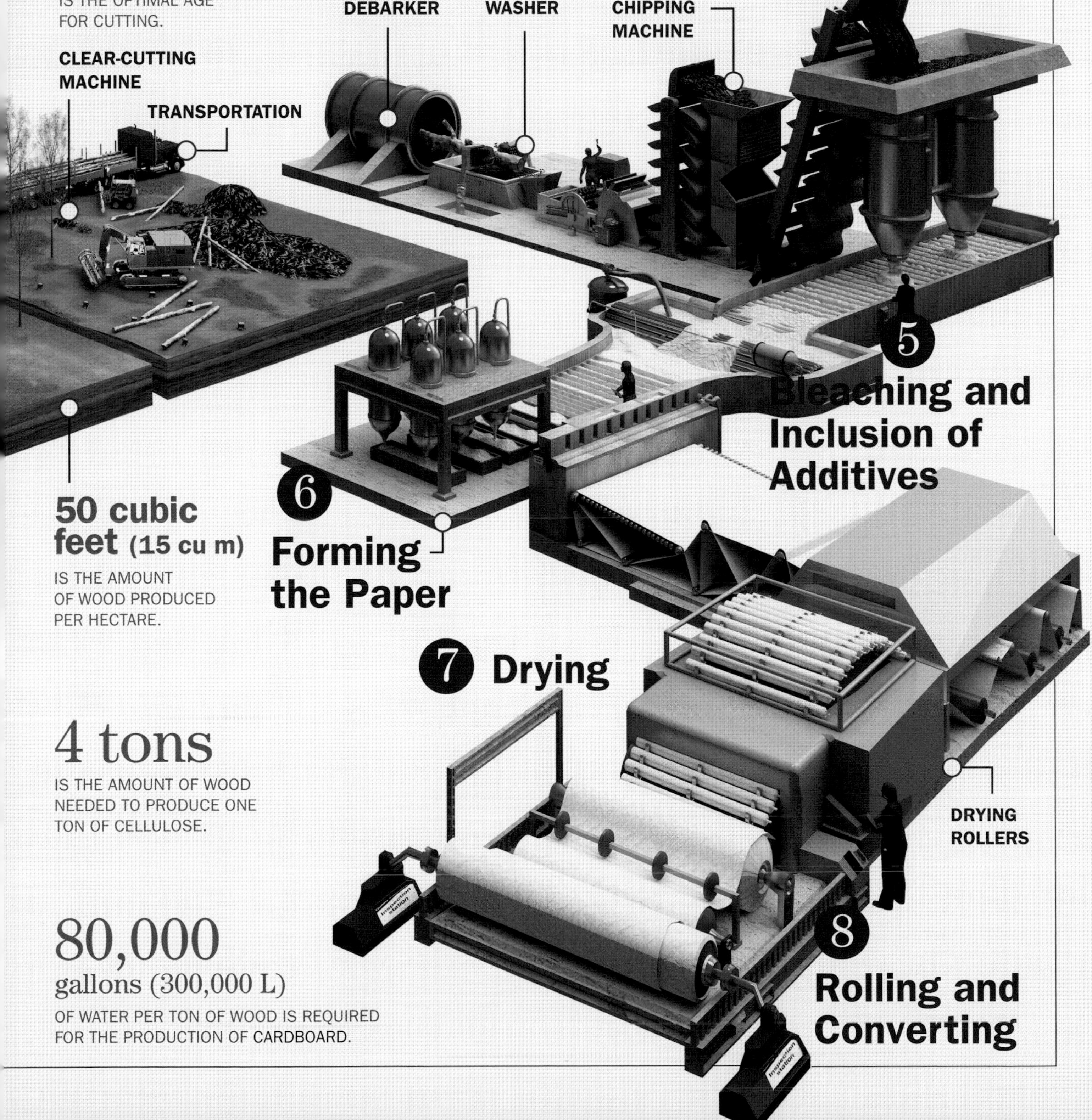

⑤ Bleaching and Inclusion of Additives

⑥ Forming the Paper

⑦ Drying

4 tons
IS THE AMOUNT OF WOOD
NEEDED TO PRODUCE ONE
TON OF CELLULOSE.

80,000
gallons (300,000 L)
OF WATER PER TON OF WOOD IS REQUIRED
FOR THE PRODUCTION OF CARDBOARD.

**DRYING
ROLLERS**

⑧ Rolling and Converting

Beekeeping

The bee is the only insect that humans have kept from antiquity for their own benefit. Thanks to beekeeping, people have been able to collect the honey that bees produce. Honey was the most widely used sweetener in Europe and Asia until the spread of sugarcane during the Middle Ages.

The Artificial Hive

It has movable panels and frames that permit extraction of the hive's products.

ROOF

LOFT

MOVABLE FRAMES

60 pounds
(25 kg) of honey

IS STORED INSIDE A HIVE SO THE BEES CAN SURVIVE THE WINTER.

SUPER
is the name given to each detachable module.

Open cells with honey

The bees deposit honey in all of the cells of the hive.

Nature's Engineering

Bees make honey out of flower nectar and pollen from the green parts of plants.

❶ The Bee's Work

Worker bees are in charge of collecting flower pollen and nectar.

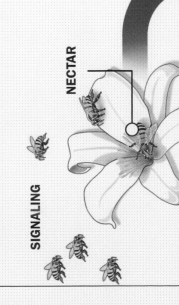

SIGNALING

NECTAR

NECTAR, HONEY'S SOURCE

Nectar is made up of 80 percent water and is secreted at the base of the flower's corolla.

30,000 bees live in a typical hive.

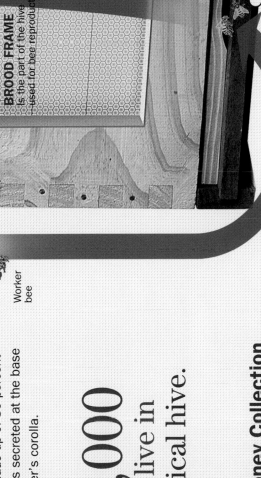

QUEEN SEPARATOR
Worker bees can pass through the separator, but the queen, which is larger, cannot.

BROOD CHAMBER

FLOOR

BROOD FRAME
Is the part of the hive used for bee reproduction.

Closed cells containing larvae

Queen bee

Worker bee

BOTTOM BOARD

OPENING

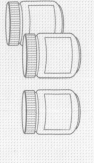

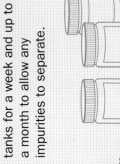

② Honey Collection

The beekeeper chooses a super, removes it from the hive, and takes out the movable frames by hand.

Hat and mask with a grille

Some are two-piece suits.

③ The Smoke

Applied by means of a smoke-producing mechanism.

Smoker

Boots

④ Extraction of the Frames

The movable frame system allows for frame removal without affecting the young brood.

From 25 to 50 pounds (11 to 23 kg) of honey are obtained from each super.

⑤ The Centrifuge

The honey is drained from the frames and separated from the wax.

Centrifuge

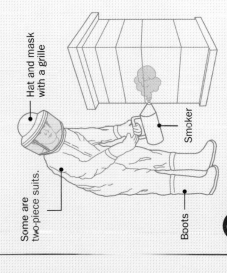

⑥ Filtering and Bottling

The honey is stored in steel tanks for a week and up to a month to allow any impurities to separate.

Bird Domesticators

The breeding of birds in captivity has great social and economic value. This activity is carried out all over the world on industrial poultry farms and family farms where birds are raised for consumption and sale. A great variety of domestic birds have been developed from species inhabiting natural environments.

Domestic birds have been bred from the following orders: Galliformes (hens, quails, turkeys, and pheasants), Anseriformes (ducks and geese), Columbiformes (pigeons), Passeriformes (canaries), and Psittaciformes (parakeets and parrots).

are colorful and melodic pets.

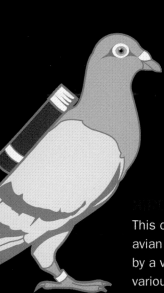

This disease, also called avian influenza A, is caused by a virus whose strains have various levels of virulence.

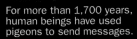

For more than 1,700 years, human beings have used pigeons to send messages.

1

Ducks carry the H5N1 virus but are immune to this disease.

2

The virus can be transmitted to the most common of domestic birds: chickens.

3

The H5N1 virus is transmitted to humans through direct contact with domestic birds.

Farm Model

When compared to other farm animals, birds grow and reproduce easily. They need to have a place with appropriate temperature, humidity, and ventilation in order to yield the desired amount of meat or eggs.

QUENCHING THIRST
The farmer provides them with water in troughs, which are placed all over the henhouse.

MIXED DIET
Birds look for insects and plant shoots as they peck the soil.

THE DOMESTICATION OF BIRDS IS A VERY OLD ACTIVITY

5000 BC	2000 BC	Before 1500
INDIA	FAR EAST	MEXICO

Milk Production

Until the 18th century, milk could be kept for only a few hours without spoiling. Only in the 20th century, after the discovery of pasteurization, allowing milk to be preserved, did milk become a universally popular drink produced industrially.

❶ MILKING AND MILK PRESERVATION AT THE FARM

❸ ANALYSIS
A test is done to determine if the milk has been heated.

❹ RECEPTION AND STERILIZATION
Milk is heated for transportation or processing, eliminating germs.

❷ COLLECTION
It is removed from the farm in large tanker trucks.

REFRIGERATED TANKER

MECHANICAL MILKING

Teat
Steel Teat Cup
Vacuum Pump —— Milk
The difference in pressure extracts the milk.
Milk Hose
Milking Stall
Pulsator Line
Teat Cups
Milk Hose

MAIN DAIRY BREEDS

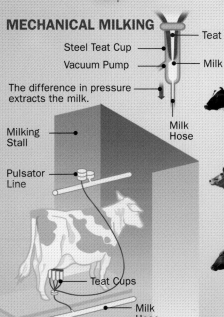

HOLSTEIN-FRIESIAN
From Germany

JERSEY
The most widespread English breed

AYRSHIRE
From southwestern Scotland

MILK PRODUCTS

CHEESE   YOGURT   BUTTER

ICE CREAM   CREAM   *DULCE DE LECHE*

⑥ HOMOGENIZATION
Ensures that the product is uniform in consistency.

⑦ PASTEURIZATION
Ensures that potentially harmful microorganisms are eliminated from the milk.

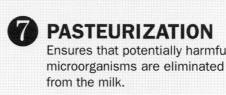

HEATING   COOLING

Milk Entrance

Hot Water
162° F (72° C)

Cold Water
39° F (4° C)

LOUIS PASTEUR
1822-95

He invented the first ways to keep substances from spoiling.

WATER HEATER

HOMOGENIZER

CONTROL ROOM

HEAT EXCHANGE

Pasteurized, Homogenized Milk Tank

Skim Milk Tank

PACKER

⑤ SEPARATION
Milk and cream are separated centrifugally. Next, milk products are obtained.

⑧ BOTTLING

SEPARATOR

FILLING MACHINE

SEALING MACHINE

Cream Tanks

ANNUAL PRODUCTION OF FRESH MILK

140 billion gallons

Black Gold

Because of its economic importance as a source of energy, petroleum, or oil, is called black gold. Searching for it requires large amounts of money and years of investigation and exploration. Once discovered, petroleum extraction entails the use of expensive machinery, which includes everything from oil pumps to refineries that convert oil into many derivative products. Petroleum is a nonrenewable source of energy.

How Petroleum Is Obtained

1 Search **2** Exploration

3 Extraction

NATURAL WAYS TO PUMP PETROLEUM

The driving force is the gas dissolved in a petroleum deposit.

The gas accumulated in the deposit pushes the petroleum outward.

Later as water is pumped in, it accumulates underneath the petroleum and pushes it upward.

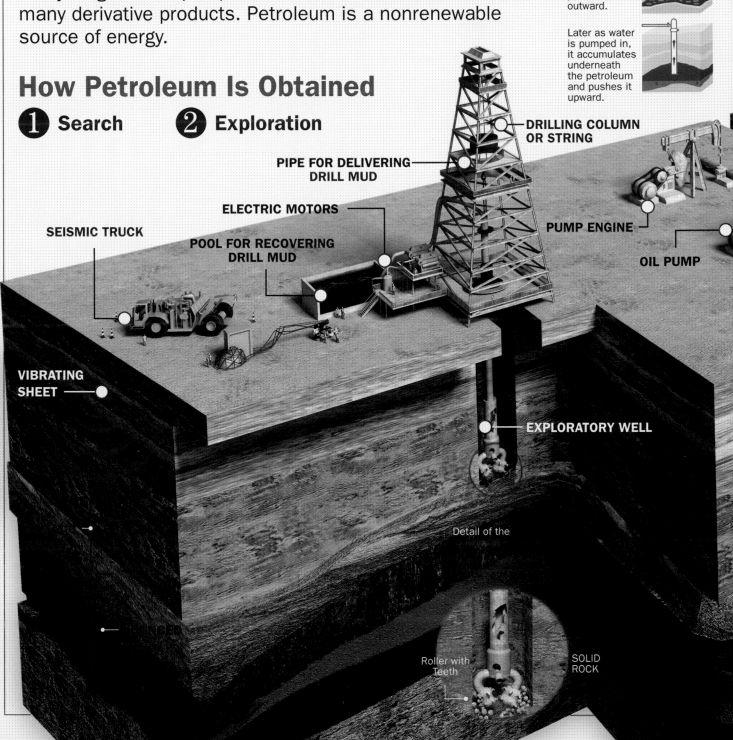

DRILLING COLUMN OR STRING

PIPE FOR DELIVERING DRILL MUD

ELECTRIC MOTORS

SEISMIC TRUCK

POOL FOR RECOVERING DRILL MUD

PUMP ENGINE

OIL PUMP

VIBRATING SHEET

EXPLORATORY WELL

Detail of the

Roller with Teeth

SOLID ROCK

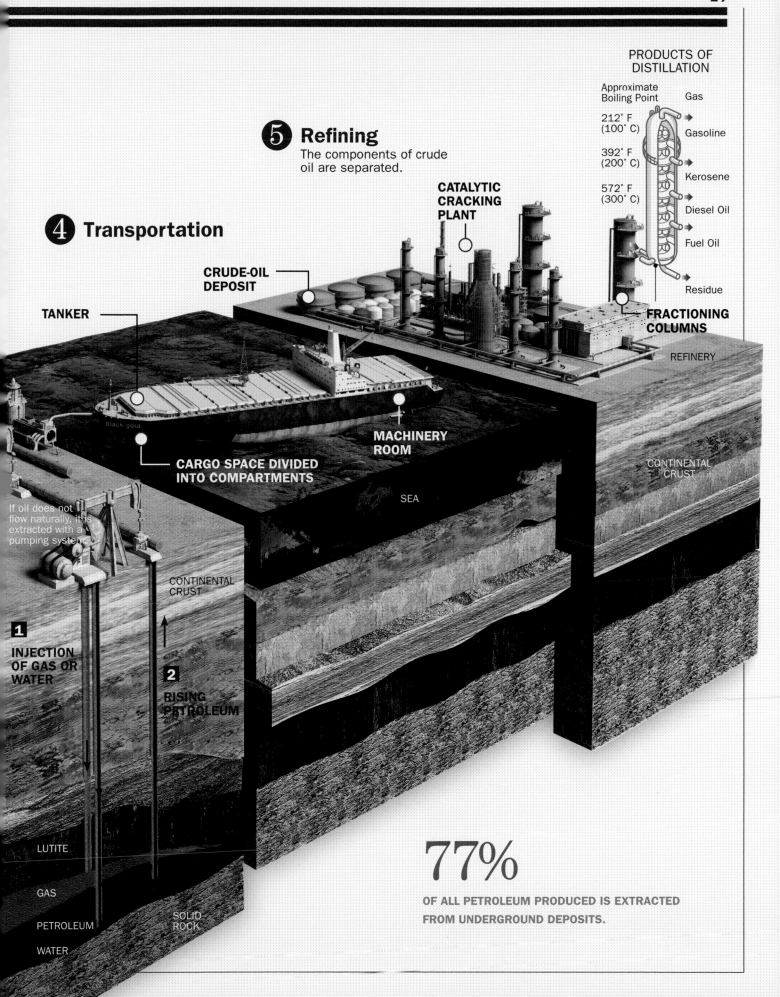

PRODUCTS OF DISTILLATION

Approximate Boiling Point — Gas

212° F (100° C) — Gasoline

392° F (200° C) — Kerosene

572° F (300° C) — Diesel Oil

Fuel Oil

Residue

⑤ **Refining**
The components of crude oil are separated.

CATALYTIC CRACKING PLANT

④ **Transportation**

CRUDE-OIL DEPOSIT

FRACTIONING COLUMNS

TANKER

REFINERY

black gold

CARGO SPACE DIVIDED INTO COMPARTMENTS

MACHINERY ROOM

CONTINENTAL CRUST

SEA

CONTINENTAL CRUST

If oil does not flow naturally, it is extracted with a pumping system.

1
INJECTION OF GAS OR WATER

2
RISING PETROLEUM

LUTITE

GAS

PETROLEUM

WATER

SOLID ROCK

77%

OF ALL PETROLEUM PRODUCED IS EXTRACTED FROM UNDERGROUND DEPOSITS.

The Automobile

Relatively few years have passed since the time of the pioneers who imagined the first "horseless carriages." Yet the automobile has established itself as one of humanity's most fundamental inventions, to the point that today it is impossible to imagine the world without it. Although it has evolved greatly in terms of efficiency and comfort, the operating principle and driving technique have changed very little since 1885, when Karl Benz presented his tricycle powered by an internal combustion engine.

A Four-Stroke Cycle

The motors of modern cars usually operate on a four-stroke cycle.

25%

THE AVERAGE EFFICIENCY OF AN INTERNAL COMBUSTION ENGINE.

Intake valve   Spark plug   Exhaust valve

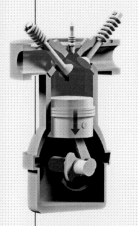  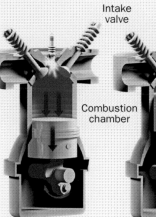 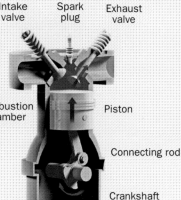

Combustion chamber

Piston

Connecting rod

Crankshaft

1ST STROKE (INTAKE)   **2ND STROKE (COMPRESSION)**   **3RD STROKE (COMBUSTION)**   **4TH STROKE (EXHAUST)**

ARRANGEMENT OF THE CYLINDERS

STRAIGHT-LINE ARRANGEMENT

V ARRANGEMENT

Milestones

1769	1885	1908	1938	1959	1971
The first self-propelled vehicle	Tricycle driven by an internal combustion engine	Ford Model T	The Volkswagen Beetle	The first car with seatbelts as standard	Motor vehicle on the Moon

Parts of the Car

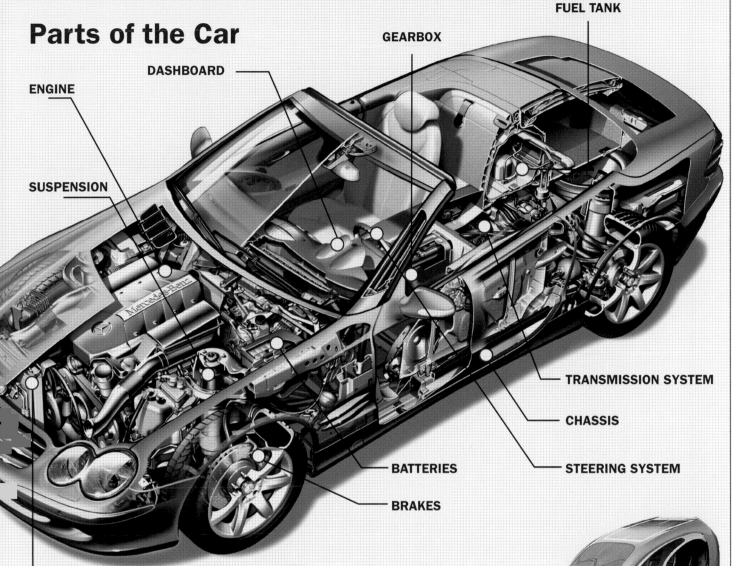

ENGINE

DASHBOARD

GEARBOX

FUEL TANK

SUSPENSION

TRANSMISSION SYSTEM

CHASSIS

BATTERIES

STEERING SYSTEM

BRAKES

RADIATOR

Alternative Fuels

Because gasoline is a nonrenewable and polluting resource, research into alternative fuels has been carried out for decades, although very few of these alternatives have taken off on a large scale.

SOLAR ENERGY

1997

The Thrust SuperSonic breaks the sound barrier.

BIOFUELS
These are produced by fermenting crops such as corn, soybeans, or sugarcane.

HYDROGEN
This is another clean, renewable fuel.

ELECTRICITY
Like hydrogen, this is a clean, renewable fuel.

Skyscrapers

The development of new materials—especially *high-performance concrete* and *steel*—has led to the design and construction of buildings to heights never achieved before. For architects and engineers who work on the construction of large skyscrapers, the greatest challenges lie in ensuring the adequate delivery of services, from elevator systems and gas and water lines to complex emergency systems. They also work to make the structures less vulnerable to potential terrorist attacks.

The Burj Khalifa

The tallest building in the world, it opened on January 4th, 2010 in the United Arab Emirates.

TECHNICAL SPECIFICATIONS

Height: 2,717 feet (828 meters)

Floors: 162

Structure: High-performance concrete reinforced with steel

Exterior: Glass with solar filters, aluminum, and stainless steel

Volume of concrete: 9,181,810 cubic feet (260,000 cu m)

Reinforced steel: 34,000 tons

FLEXIBILITY

Strong winds can cause tall skyscrapers to sway.

Height	Sway
1,985 feet (605 m)	5 feet (1.5 m)
1,870 feet (570 m)	4 feet (1.25 m)
1,450 feet (442 m)	2.5 feet (.75 m)
1,230 feet (375 m)	2 feet (.5 m)

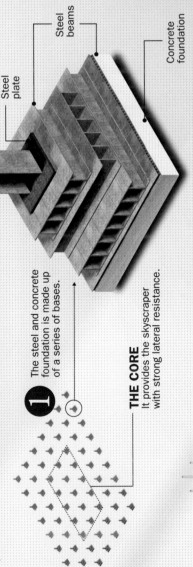

From the Ground to the Sky

The construction of a skyscraper begins with the digging of a large pit for the foundation that will support the entire edifice.

1 The steel and concrete foundation is made up of a series of bases.

THE CORE
It provides the skyscraper with strong lateral resistance.

THE FOUNDATION

Steel column

Steel plate

Steel beams

Concrete foundation

REINFORCED CONCRETE

2 The weight of the building rests upon columns.

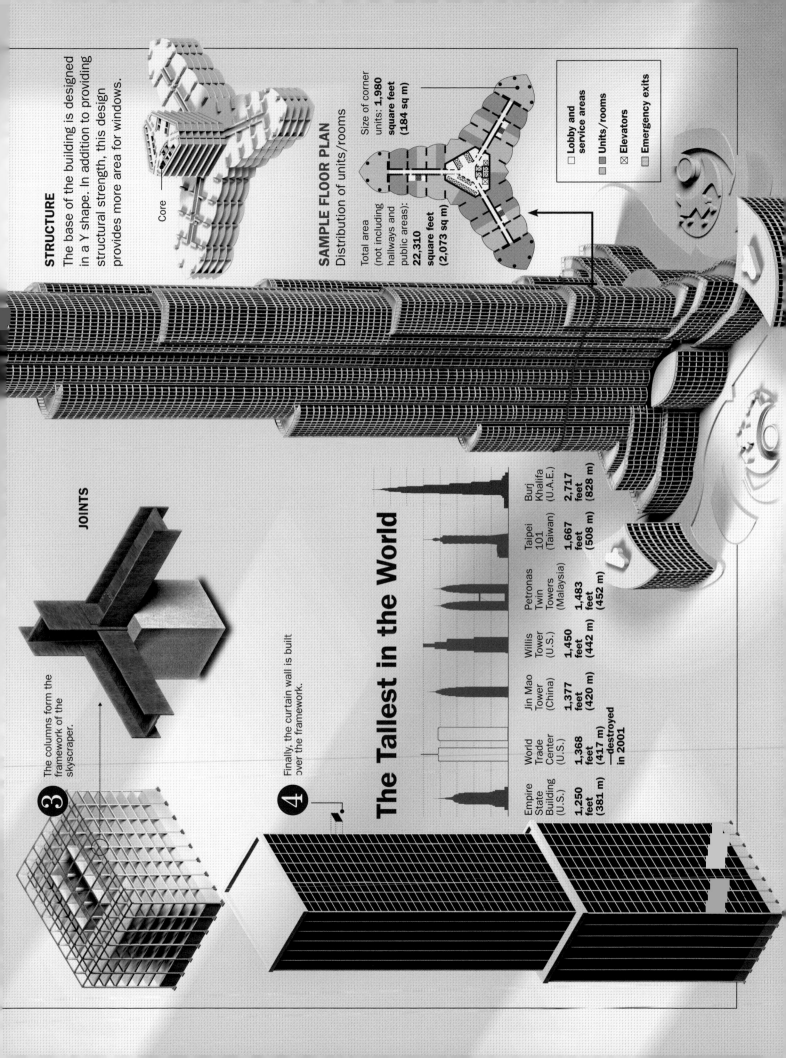

STRUCTURE

The base of the building is designed in a Y shape. In addition to providing structural strength, this design provides more area for windows.

Core

SAMPLE FLOOR PLAN
Distribution of units/rooms

Total area (not including hallways and public areas): **22,310 square feet (2,073 sq m)**

Size of corner units: **1,980 square feet (184 sq m)**

☐ Lobby and service areas
▨ Units/rooms
⊠ Elevators
▥ Emergency exits

JOINTS

3 The columns form the framework of the skyscraper.

4 Finally, the curtain wall is built over the framework.

The Tallest in the World

	Empire State Building (U.S.)	World Trade Center (U.S.)	Jin Mao Tower (China)	Willis Tower (U.S.)	Petronas Twin Towers (Malaysia)	Taipei 101 (Taiwan)	Burj Khalifa (U.A.E.)
	1,250 feet (381 m)	**1,368 feet (417 m)** —destroyed in 2001	**1,377 feet (420 m)**	**1,450 feet (442 m)**	**1,483 feet (452 m)**	**1,667 feet (508 m)**	**2,717 feet (828 m)**

Computers and the Internet

From the huge calculating machines that occupied entire rooms to today's home and laptop models, computers have revolutionized how we see the world and relate to it. Today our everyday lives are characterized by information technology, whether for recreation, work, study, or communication. The Internet is a worldwide network where interconnected computers can exchange information.

The Personal Computer

is made up of various interconnected devices (the hardware) and programs (the software). The core is a very powerful microprocessor that contains all the devices and is installed on the *motherboard*.

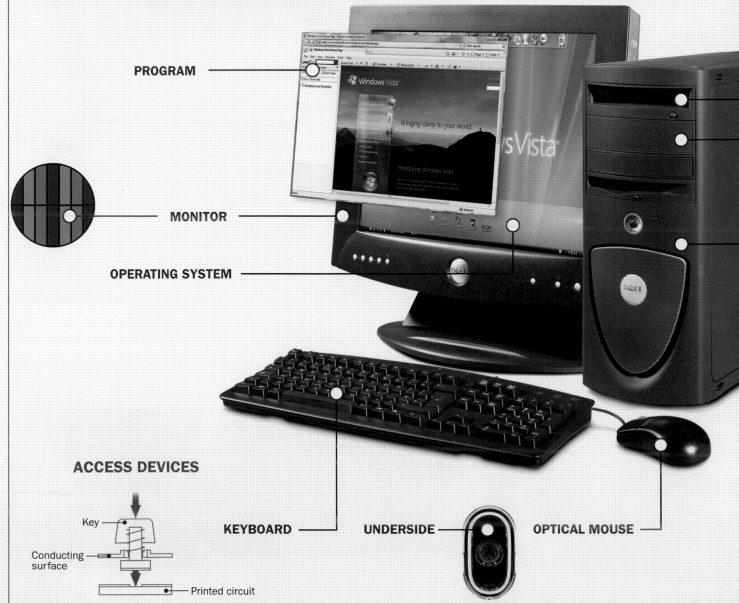

PROGRAM

MONITOR

OPERATING SYSTEM

ACCESS DEVICES

Key

Conducting surface

Printed circuit

KEYBOARD

UNDERSIDE

OPTICAL MOUSE

How a Computer Works

1 INPUT

2 MICROPROCESSOR

3 RAM MEMORY

4 PROCESSING

5 STORAGE

6 OUTPUT

STORAGE DEVICES

CD/DVD READER/RECORDER

HARD DISK

COMPUTER TOWER

CONNECTORS

USB PORT

PARALLEL PORT

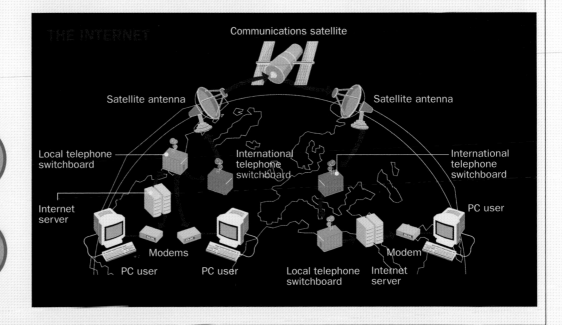

THE INTERNET

Communications satellite

Satellite antenna

Satellite antenna

Local telephone switchboard

International telephone switchboard

International telephone switchboard

Internet server

PC user

Modems

PC user

PC user

Local telephone switchboard

Internet server

Modem

PC user

Artificial Intelligence

Although the concept of artificial intelligence (AI) had long been present in science fiction, its theoretical basis was not established until the early 1950s. At first, investigators in the discipline tackled the problem with great optimism, but over the years the challenge of creating a machine that could "feel" and behave like a human being revealed its considerable complexity. Today there are amazing robots that still lack these human qualities.

Man's Best Friend

AIBO is one of the most complex robot pets ever created.

LEDS

TOUCH

MULTITALENTED

DIMENSIONS

10.9 inches (27.8 cm)

12.5 inches (31.7 cm)

Happy	Angry	Sad
Recognized its owner	Detected an obstacle	Has been petted
Petted by its owner	Favorite spot	Favorite things

AI Development

1950	1956	1966	1973	1994	1996
The Turing test is published. The purpose of the test is to determine whether a machine can be considered intelligent.	The researcher John McCarthy coins the term "artificial intelligence."	The computer program ELIZA could interact with users.	Freddy, a robot capable of identifying and assembling objects	The twin cars VaMP and VITA-2	Deep Blue wins a game of chess.

The Day a Machine Beat the Best Human

On February 10, 1996, an IBM computer called Deep Blue won a game of chess in a match against the world chess champion, Garry Kasparov, becoming thereby the first computer to triumph over a reigning world champion.

It has a 52-volt lithium-ion battery mounted in its backpack.

The robot can run at a speed of 3.7 miles (6 km) per hour and walk at 1.7 miles (2.7 km) an hour.

Humanoids

Their humanlike appearance could spark our imagination and reinforce the impression that the humanoid is a living machine.

PAPERO ▶

Produced by NEC, PaPeRo is a domestic robot that can recognize the faces of its family members, distinguish colors, read text, dance, and change a TV channel when its owner gives a verbal command.

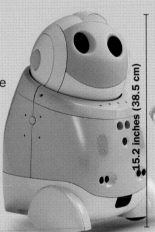

15.2 inches (38.5 cm)

The robot can lift up to 1 pound (0.5 kg) in each hand.

ASIMO ◀

Honda's bipedal robot ASIMO can walk, dance, shake hands, carry a tray of drinks like a waiter, and answer simple questions.

1998

Furby, a small pet that resembles a gremlin

1999

Kismet, one of the first robots to respond to people in a natural manner

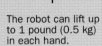

2003

Qrio, the first bipedal robot capable of running

Water and Fluids

Water makes up almost two thirds of the human body by weight. Water is present in all the tissues of the body. It serves as the basis of the circulatory system, which uses blood to distribute nutrients to the entire body. Moreover, water helps maintain body temperature by expelling excess heat through the skin via perspiration and evaporation.

Water Balance

In its continuous process of taking in and eliminating water, one of the most important functions of the body is to maintain a continuous equilibrium between the water that enters and the water that leaves the body.

60%

THE PERCENTAGE OF A PERSON'S WEIGHT THAT IS DUE TO WATER

HOW THIRST IS CONTROLLED

Thirst is the sensation through which the nervous system informs its major organ, the brain, that the body needs water. The control center is the hypothalamus.

HOW WATER IS ABSORBED

50%
of the water comes from ingesting fluids.

35%
of the water is obtained from food.

15%
comes from metabolic activities.

HOW WATER IS ELIMINATED

60%
is eliminated with urine.

18%
is eliminated by sweating and through evaporation from the skin.

14%
is eliminated during exhalation by the lungs.

8%
is eliminated in excrement.

Chemical Elements

The body contains many chemical elements. The most common are oxygen, hydrogen, carbon, and nitrogen. Nine chemical elements are present in moderate amounts, and the rest are present only in very small amounts, so they are called trace elements.

 IRON 0.004%

 MAGNESIUM 0.05%   **CALCIUM 1.5%**

 SODIUM 0.15%   **CHLORINE 0.2%**

 IODINE 0.0004%

 POTASSIUM 0.3%   **PHOSPHORUS 1%**

SULFUR 0.3%

Proteins

Proteins are formed through the combination of the four most common chemical elements found in the body.

C 18% CARBON

H 10% HYDROGEN

N 3% NITROGEN

O 65% OXYGEN

The Cell

The cell is the smallest unit of the human body—and of all living organisms—able to function by itself. It is so small that it can be seen only with a microscope. Its essential parts are the nucleus and cytoplasm, which are surrounded by a membrane. Each cell reproduces independently through a process called *mitosis*. The human body has millions of cells, organized into tissues and organs.

Cell Theory

Before the invention of the microscope, it was impossible to see cells. The development of the microscope made detailed observation of the internal structure of the cell possible. In 1838 Mathias Schleiden observed living cells, and in 1839, in collaboration with Theodor Schwann, he developed the first theory of cells: that all living organisms consist of cells.

THEODOR SCHWANN

MATHIAS SCHLEIDEN

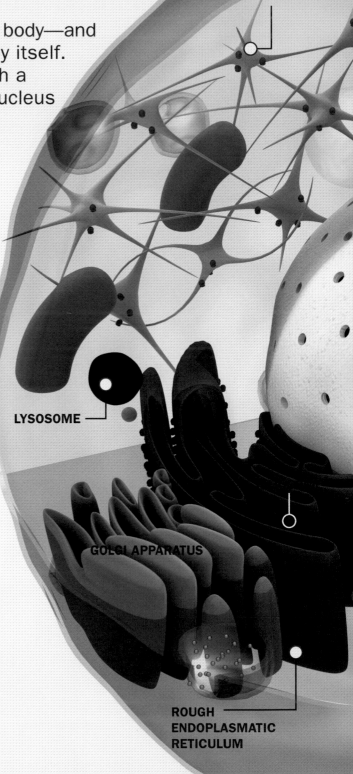

CYTOSKELETON

LYSOSOME

GOLGI APPARATUS

ROUGH ENDOPLASMATIC RETICULUM

UNDER THE MICROSCOPE

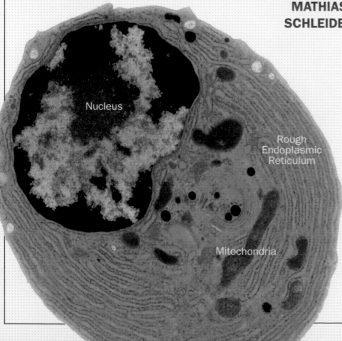

Nucleus

Rough Endoplasmic Reticulum

Mitochondria

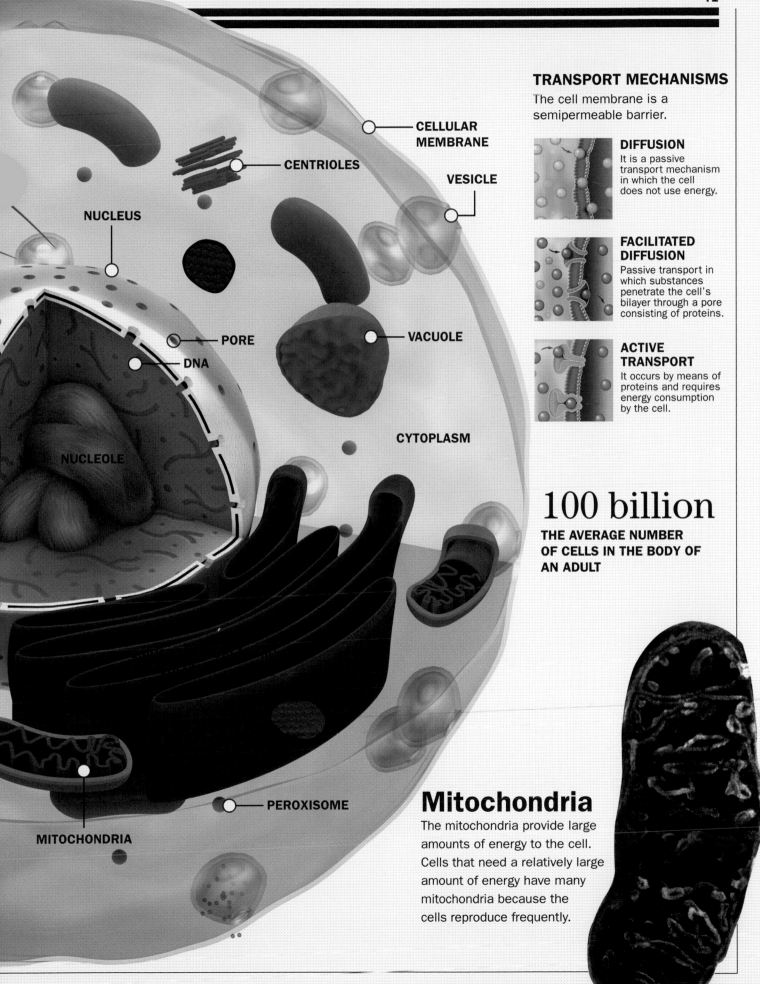

CELLULAR MEMBRANE

CENTRIOLES

VESICLE

NUCLEUS

PORE

DNA

VACUOLE

NUCLEOLE

CYTOPLASM

MITOCHONDRIA

PEROXISOME

TRANSPORT MECHANISMS
The cell membrane is a semipermeable barrier.

DIFFUSION
It is a passive transport mechanism in which the cell does not use energy.

FACILITATED DIFFUSION
Passive transport in which substances penetrate the cell's bilayer through a pore consisting of proteins.

ACTIVE TRANSPORT
It occurs by means of proteins and requires energy consumption by the cell.

100 billion
THE AVERAGE NUMBER OF CELLS IN THE BODY OF AN ADULT

Mitochondria
The mitochondria provide large amounts of energy to the cell. Cells that need a relatively large amount of energy have many mitochondria because the cells reproduce frequently.

Skeleton

The skeleton, or the skeletal system, is a strong, resistant structure made up of bones and their supporting *ligaments* and *cartilage*. The skeleton gives the body form and structure, covers and protects the internal organs, and makes movement possible. The bones store minerals and produce blood cells in the bone marrow.

Well-Defined Form

The structure of the skeleton can be described as a vertical column of chained vertebrae with a pair of limbs at each end and topped off by the cranium. The upper limbs, or arms, are connected to the shoulder blades and clavicles in what is called the scapular belt, and the lower limbs, or legs, are connected at the hips, or pelvic belt.

Leonardo

LEONARDO DA VINCI WAS ONE OF THE FIRST TO MAKE PRECISE DRAWINGS OF HUMAN BONES.

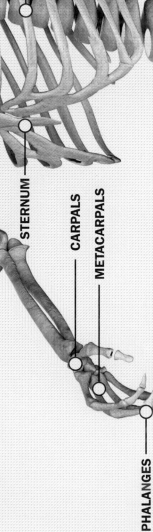

CRANIUM

OCCIPITAL BONE

INFERIOR MAXILLARY

SPINAL COLUMN

CLAVICLE

SHOULDER BLADE

HUMERUS

RADIUS

CUBITUM

RIBS

ILIUM

SACRUM

STERNUM

CARPALS

METACARPALS

PELVIS

PHALANGES

Types of Bones

SHORT BONES: have a spherical or conical shape.

LONG BONES: have a central section that lies between two end points.

FLAT BONES: form thin bony plates.

IRREGULAR BONES: take various shapes.

SESAMOID BONES: are small and round.

208 bones

THE TOTAL NUMBER OF BONES IN THE BODY IS BETWEEN 206 AND 208, DEPENDING ON THE INDIVIDUAL.

COCCYX (TAILBONE)

0.12 inches (3 mm)

THE LENGTH OF THE SHORTEST BONE OF THE BODY. IT IS THE STIRRUP, A BONE IN THE EAR.

CALCANUM

PHALANGES

KNEECAP

FEMUR

FIBULA

TIBIA

TARSALS

METATARSALS

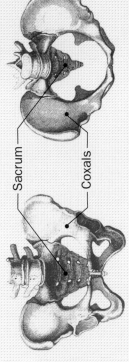

Sacrum

Coxals

Sexual Differences

Bone structure is basically the same for both sexes. In women, though, the center opening of the pelvis is larger in order for an infant's head to pass through it during childbirth.

Cranium and Face

The cranium surrounds and protects the brain, cerebellum, and cerebral trunk. In an adult the cranium consists of eight bones that form the skull and the base of the cranium. The face consists of 14 bones, all of which are fixed except the lower maxillary, which makes up the mandible. The total number of bones in the head as a whole exceeds the total of the face and cranium (22) because it includes the little bones of the middle ear.

Sutures and Fontanels

The cranium consists of separate bones at birth and closes completely at maturity. The narrow separations between the bones, which appear as lines in the fetus for the first months of its life, are called sutures. Spaces called fontanels form where the sutures meet.

9 pounds (4 kg)
THE WEIGHT OF AN ADULT HUMAN HEAD

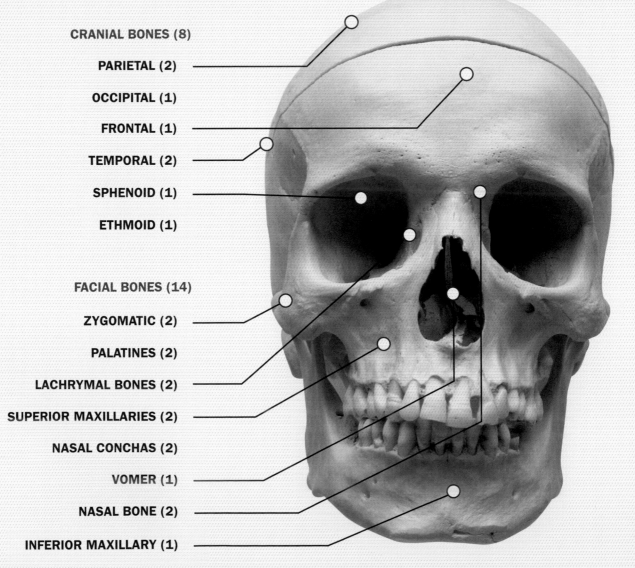

CRANIAL BONES (8)

PARIETAL (2)

OCCIPITAL (1)

FRONTAL (1)

TEMPORAL (2)

SPHENOID (1)

ETHMOID (1)

FACIAL BONES (14)

ZYGOMATIC (2)

PALATINES (2)

LACHRYMAL BONES (2)

SUPERIOR MAXILLARIES (2)

NASAL CONCHAS (2)

VOMER (1)

NASAL BONE (2)

INFERIOR MAXILLARY (1)

Bony Tissue

The primary mission of the bones is to protect the organs of the body. Bones are solid and resilient, which allows them to endure blows and prevent damage to the internal organs. The hard exterior is balanced by the internal spongy part. Over a person's lifetime bones are continuously regenerated; this process continues even after a person reaches maturity. Besides supporting the body and enabling movement, the bones are charged with producing red globules: thousands of millions of new cells are produced daily in the bone marrow, in a never-ending process of replacing old cells.

Bone Structure

All the hard parts that form the skeleton in vertebrates, such as the human being, are called bones. They may be hard, but they are nevertheless formed by a structure of living cells, nerves, and blood vessels, and they are capable of withstanding pressure of up to 1,000 pounds (450 kg). Because of their constitution and characteristics, they can mend themselves when fractured.

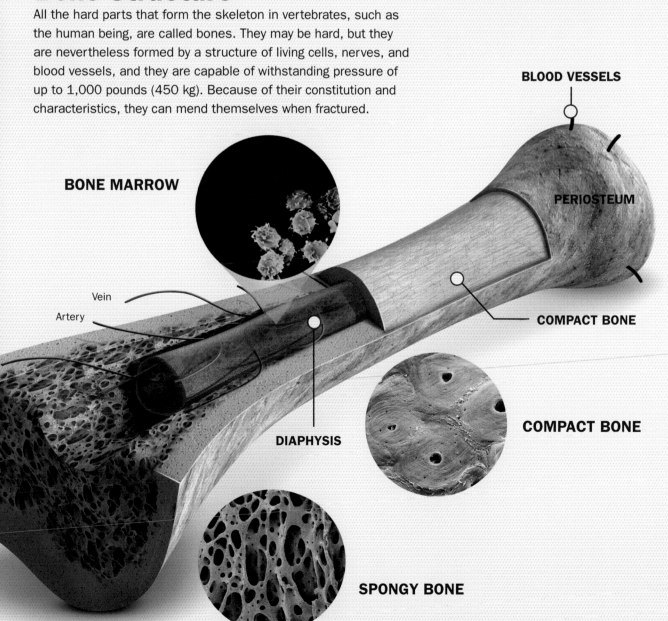

BLOOD VESSELS

BONE MARROW

PERIOSTEUM

Vein

Artery

COMPACT BONE

DIAPHYSIS

COMPACT BONE

SPONGY BONE

The Great Axis of the Body

The vertebral, or spinal, column is the flexible axis that lends support to the body. It consists of a series of bones jointed together in a line, or chain, called the vertebrae. The spinal column forms a protective inner channel through which the spinal cord runs. The ribs perform a similar function, wrapping and shielding the vital internal organs, which include the heart and lungs.

ATLAS

AXIS

CERVICAL

THORACIC, OR DORSAL, VERTEBRAE

The Three Curves

The three types of natural curvature in the spinal column include cervical lordosis (forward, or inward, bending in the cervical region of the spine), kyphosis (outward bending of the thoracic region of the spine), and lumbar lordosis (forward bending of the lower back). Shown here is the right side of the spinal column.

The Spinal Column

The vertebrae have a centrum that allows them to support the body's weight, each vertebra upon the next, as well as the weight of the rest of the body.

THE RIBS AND THE RIB CAGE

The 12 pairs of ribs extend from the spinal column.

33 bones

OR VERTEBRAE, MAKE UP THE SPINAL COLUMN.

Rib Cartilage

Sternum

Heart

Diaphragm

Spleen

Lung

Liver

Stomach

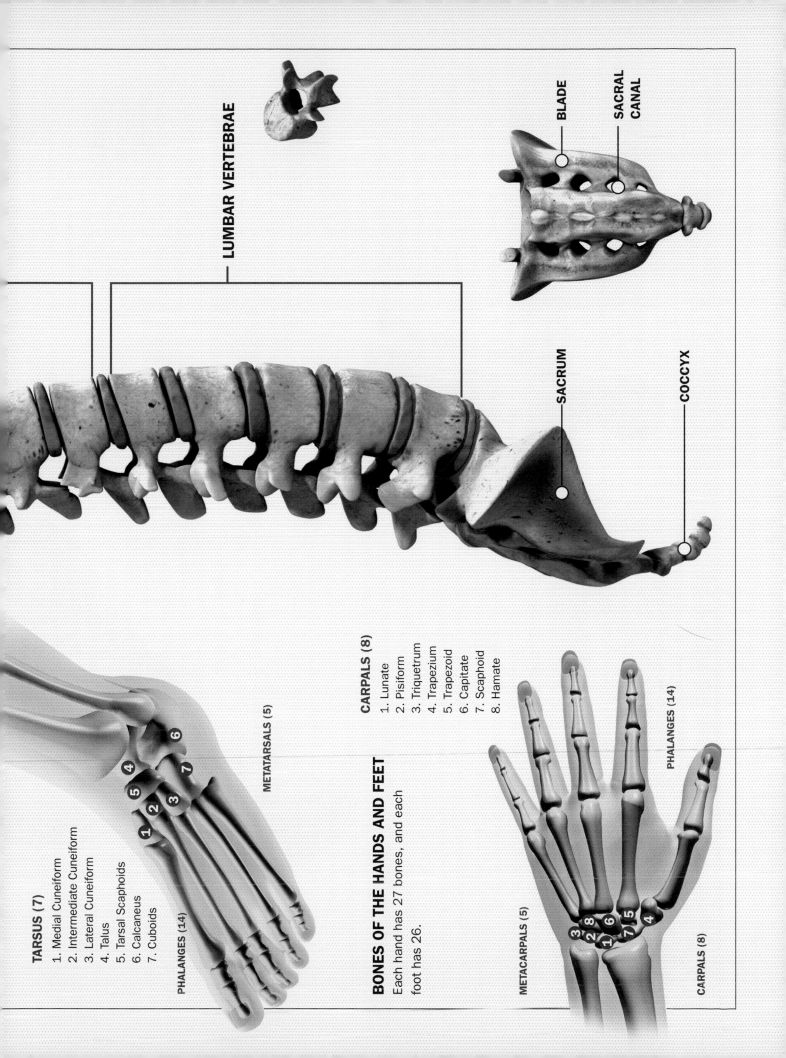

LUMBAR VERTEBRAE

BLADE

SACRAL CANAL

SACRUM

COCCYX

TARSUS (7)

1. Medial Cuneiform
2. Intermediate Cuneiform
3. Lateral Cuneiform
4. Talus
5. Tarsal Scaphoids
6. Calcaneus
7. Cuboids

PHALANGES (14)

METATARSALS (5)

BONES OF THE HANDS AND FEET

Each hand has 27 bones; and each foot has 26.

CARPALS (8)

1. Lunate
2. Pisiform
3. Triquetrum
4. Trapezium
5. Trapezoid
6. Capitate
7. Scaphoid
8. Hamate

PHALANGES (14)

METACARPALS (5)

CARPALS (8)

Muscular System

The muscles are organs formed by fleshy tissue consisting of contractile cells. They are divided into striated, smooth, and cardiac (the muscular tissue of the heart). Muscles shape and protect the organism.

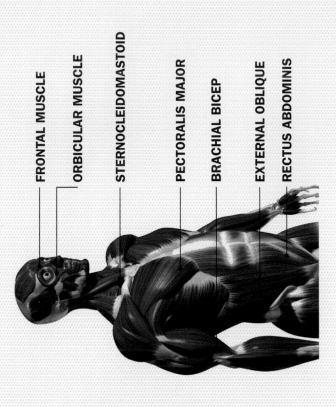

- FRONTAL MUSCLE
- ORBICULAR MUSCLE
- STERNOCLEIDOMASTOID
- PECTORALIS MAJOR
- BRACHIAL BICEP
- EXTERNAL OBLIQUE
- RECTUS ABDOMINIS

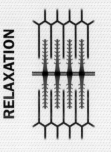

RELAXATION

CONTRACTION

650 skeletal muscles

OR VOLUNTARY MUSCLES ARE IN THE TYPICAL HUMAN BODY.

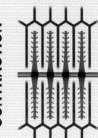

- OCCIPITAL
- SPLENIUS
- TRAPEZIUM
- DELTOID
- BRACHIAL TRICEP

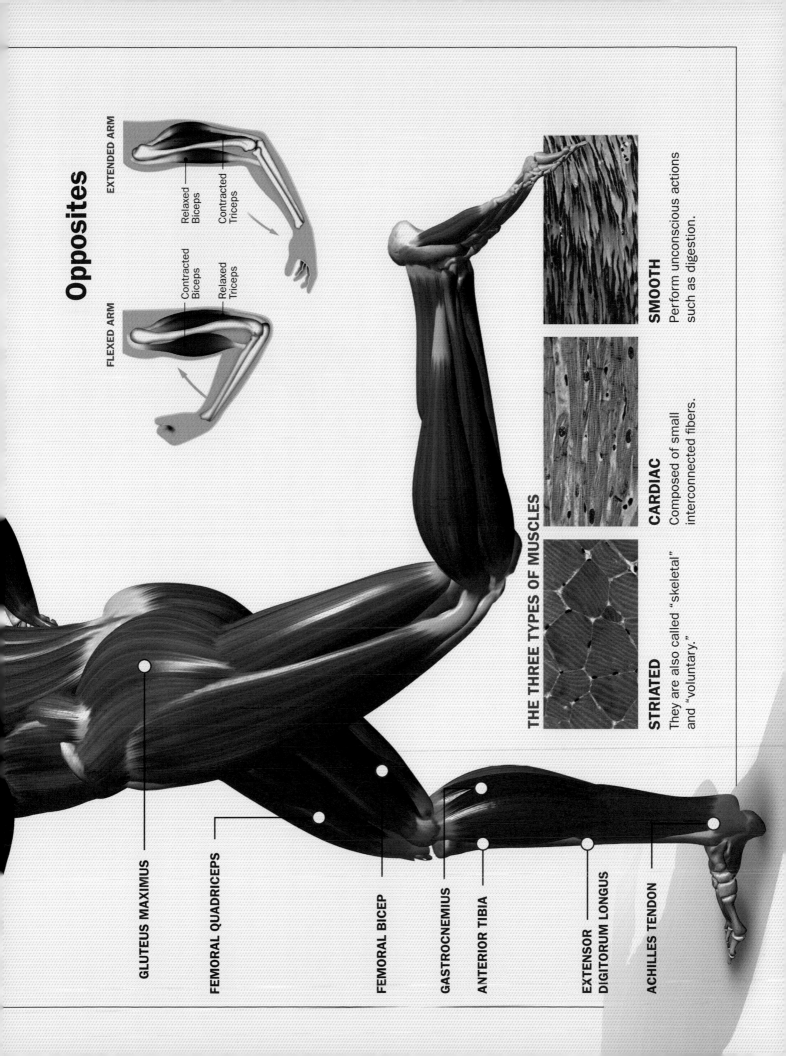

Opposites

FLEXED ARM

Contracted Biceps

Relaxed Triceps

EXTENDED ARM

Relaxed Biceps

Contracted Triceps

THE THREE TYPES OF MUSCLES

STRIATED
They are also called "skeletal" and "voluntary."

CARDIAC
Composed of small interconnected fibers.

SMOOTH
Perform unconscious actions such as digestion.

GLUTEUS MAXIMUS

FEMORAL QUADRICEPS

FEMORAL BICEP

GASTROCNEMIUS

ANTERIOR TIBIA

EXTENSOR DIGITORUM LONGUS

ACHILLES TENDON

Circulatory System

Its function is to carry blood to and from all the organs of the body. To drive the constant movement of the blood, the system uses the pumping of the heart. The arteries bring oxygen-rich blood to all the cells, and the veins retrieve the blood so that it can be oxygenated once again and so that wastes can be removed.

A System That Goes Around

The center of the system is the heart, which, together with a network of vessels, forms the cardiovascular machinery. Beginning at the heart, the circulatory system completes two circuits: the main, or systemic, circulation via the aortic artery and the minor, or pulmonary, circulation.

BLOOD DISTRIBUTION DURING CIRCULATION

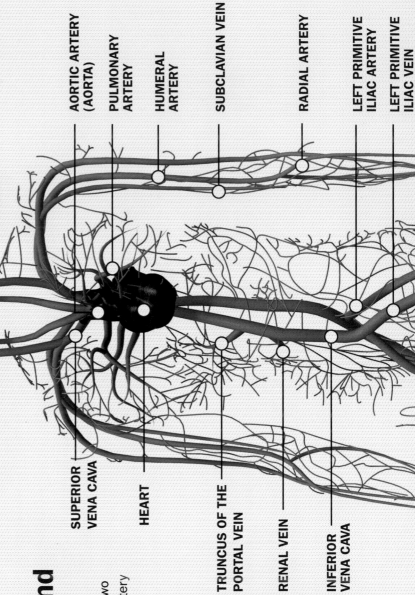

1 inch
(2.5 cm)

THE EXTERNAL DIAMETER OF THE AORTA (THE LARGEST ARTERY) AND THE VENA CAVA (THE LARGEST VEIN)

TEMPORAL ARTERY

TEMPORAL VEIN

JUGULAR VEINS

LEFT CAROTID ARTERY

AORTIC ARTERY (AORTA)

PULMONARY ARTERY

HUMERAL ARTERY

SUBCLAVIAN VEIN

RADIAL ARTERY

LEFT PRIMITIVE ILIAC ARTERY

LEFT PRIMITIVE ILIAC VEIN

SUPERIOR VENA CAVA

HEART

TRUNCUS OF THE PORTAL VEIN

RENAL VEIN

INFERIOR VENA CAVA

67% Veins

17% Arteries

11% Heart

5% Capillaries

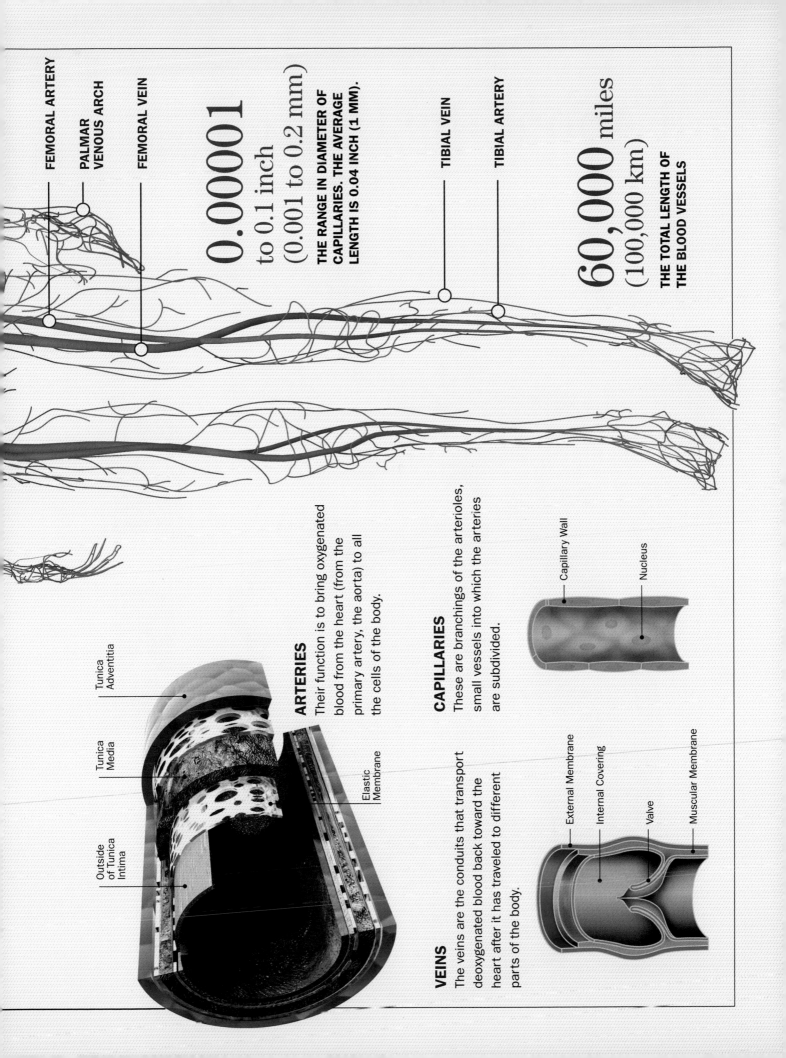

FEMORAL ARTERY

PALMAR VENOUS ARCH

FEMORAL VEIN

0.00001
to 0.1 inch
(0.001 to 0.2 mm)

THE RANGE IN DIAMETER OF CAPILLARIES. THE AVERAGE LENGTH IS 0.04 INCH (1 MM).

TIBIAL VEIN

TIBIAL ARTERY

60,000 miles
(100,000 km)

THE TOTAL LENGTH OF THE BLOOD VESSELS

Tunica Adventitia

Tunica Media

Outside of Tunica Intima

Elastic Membrane

ARTERIES

Their function is to bring oxygenated blood from the heart (from the primary artery, the aorta) to all the cells of the body.

CAPILLARIES

These are branchings of the arterioles, small vessels into which the arteries are subdivided.

Capillary Wall

Nucleus

VEINS

The veins are the conduits that transport deoxygenated blood back toward the heart after it has traveled to different parts of the body.

External Membrane

Internal Covering

Valve

Muscular Membrane

All About the Heart

The heart is the engine of the circulatory apparatus: it supplies 10 pints (4.7 L) of blood per minute. Its rhythmic pumping ensures that blood arrives in every part of the body. The heart beats between 60 and 100 times per minute in a person at rest and up to 200 times per minute during activity. The heart is a hollow organ, the size of a fist; it is enclosed in the thoracic cavity in the center of the chest above the diaphragm.

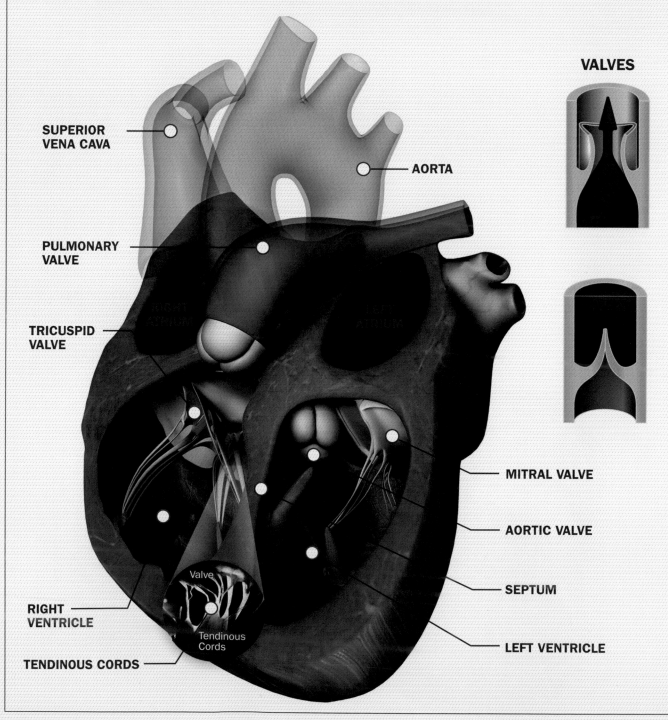

VALVES

SUPERIOR VENA CAVA

AORTA

PULMONARY VALVE

TRICUSPID VALVE

RIGHT ATRIUM

LEFT ATRIUM

MITRAL VALVE

AORTIC VALVE

SEPTUM

RIGHT VENTRICLE

Valve

Tendinous Cords

LEFT VENTRICLE

TENDINOUS CORDS

Components of the Blood

The blood is a liquid tissue composed of water, dissolved substances, and blood cells. The blood circulates inside the blood vessels thanks to the impulse it receives from the contraction of the heart. A principal function of the blood is to distribute nutrients to all the cells of the body. For example, the red blood cells carry oxygen. The blood also contains white blood cells and platelets that protect the body in various ways.

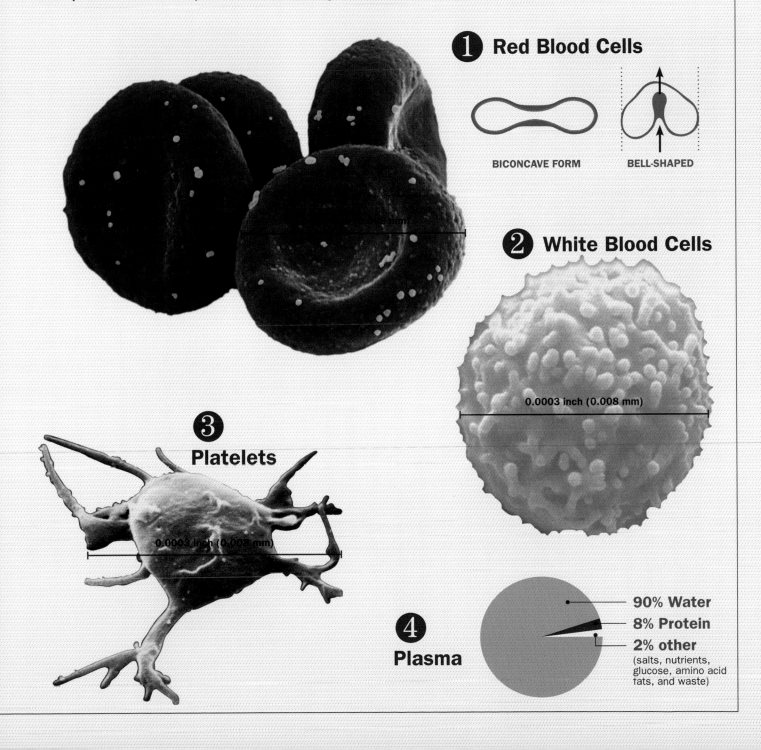

❶ Red Blood Cells

BICONCAVE FORM   BELL-SHAPED

❷ White Blood Cells

0.0003 inch (0.008 mm)

❸ Platelets

0.0003 inch (0.003 mm)

❹ Plasma

90% Water
8% Protein
2% other
(salts, nutrients, glucose, amino acid fats, and waste)

Lymphatic System

The lymphatic system defends against foreign organisms and aids with transport of liquid and matter via the circulation of a liquid known as lymph. Lymph nodes, or glands, are distributed throughout the body. The battle of the immune system against invading germs takes place within the nodes.

Natural Defenses

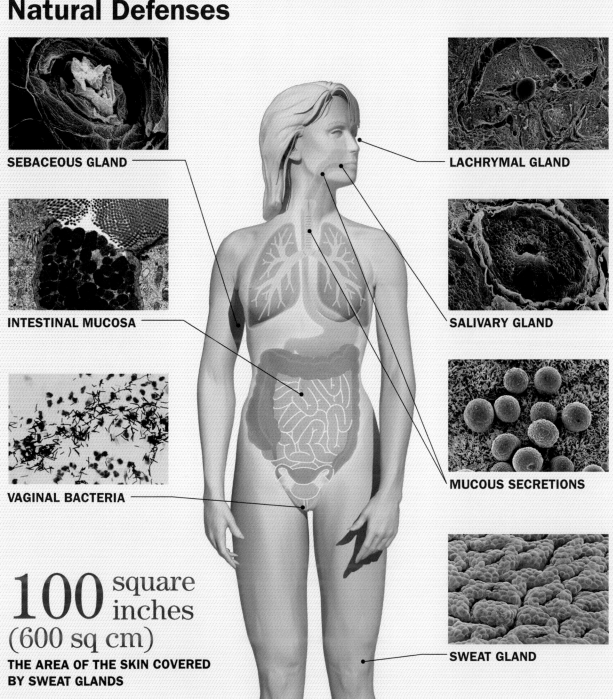

SEBACEOUS GLAND

INTESTINAL MUCOSA

VAGINAL BACTERIA

LACHRYMAL GLAND

SALIVARY GLAND

MUCOUS SECRETIONS

SWEAT GLAND

100 square inches (600 sq cm)

THE AREA OF THE SKIN COVERED BY SWEAT GLANDS

Invaders

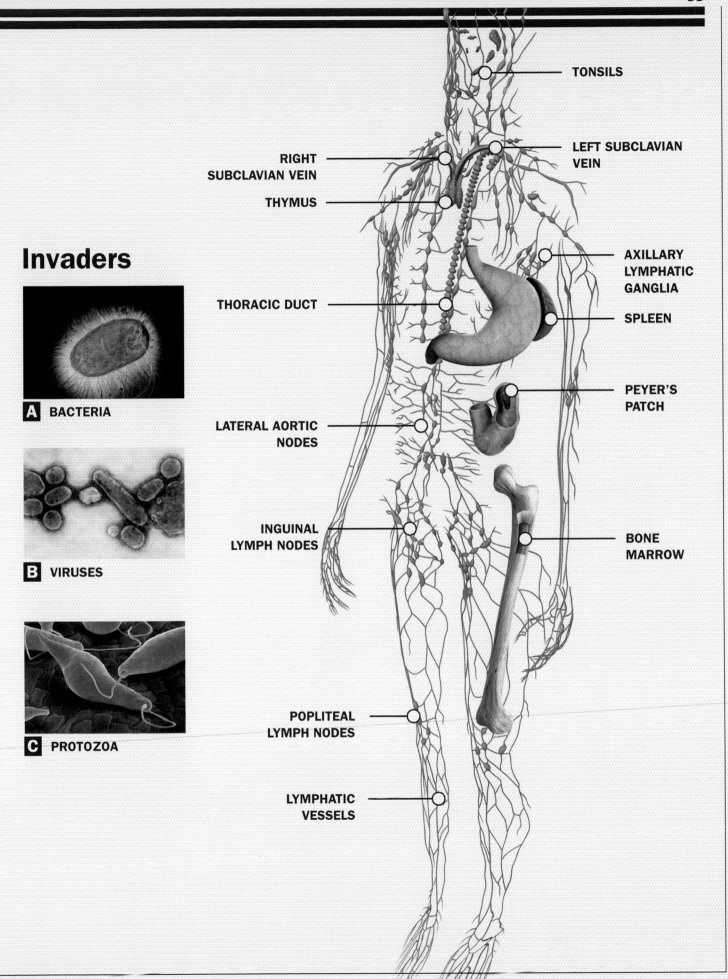

A BACTERIA

B VIRUSES

C PROTOZOA

TONSILS

RIGHT SUBCLAVIAN VEIN

LEFT SUBCLAVIAN VEIN

THYMUS

AXILLARY LYMPHATIC GANGLIA

THORACIC DUCT

SPLEEN

PEYER'S PATCH

LATERAL AORTIC NODES

INGUINAL LYMPH NODES

BONE MARROW

POPLITEAL LYMPH NODES

LYMPHATIC VESSELS

Respiratory System

The respiratory system organizes and activates respiration, a process by which the human body takes in air from the atmosphere, extracts the oxygen that the circulation will bring to all the cells, and returns to the air products it does not need, such as carbon dioxide. The basic steps are inhalation, through which air enters the nose and mouth, and exhalation, through which air is expelled. Respiration involves the airway that begins in the nose and continues through the pharynx, larynx, trachea, bronchi, bronchioles, and alveoli. The oxygen is then distributed to the entire body via the blood.

6 quarts (5.5 l)

THE APPROXIMATE VOLUME OF AIR THAT ENTERS AND EXITS THE LUNGS DURING ONE MINUTE OF BREATHING

15

WE NORMALLY BREATHE BETWEEN 15 AND 16 TIMES A MINUTE.

WHAT ENTERS AND WHAT EXITS

Component	Percentage of Inhaled Air	Percentage of Exhaled Air
Nitrogen	78.6	78.6
Oxygen	20.8	15.6
Carbon Dioxide	0.04	4
Water Vapor	0.56	1.8
Total	**100**	**100**

Intercostal Muscles

Hollow structures that terminate in the bronchioles. They store air, have the form of a globe or cluster of bubbles, and are active in gas exchange.

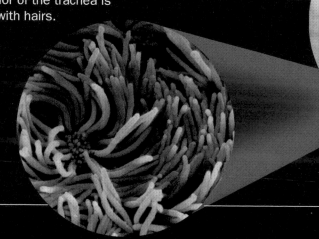

The resonance box that houses the vocal cords

The interior of the trachea is covered with hairs.

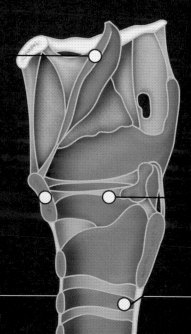

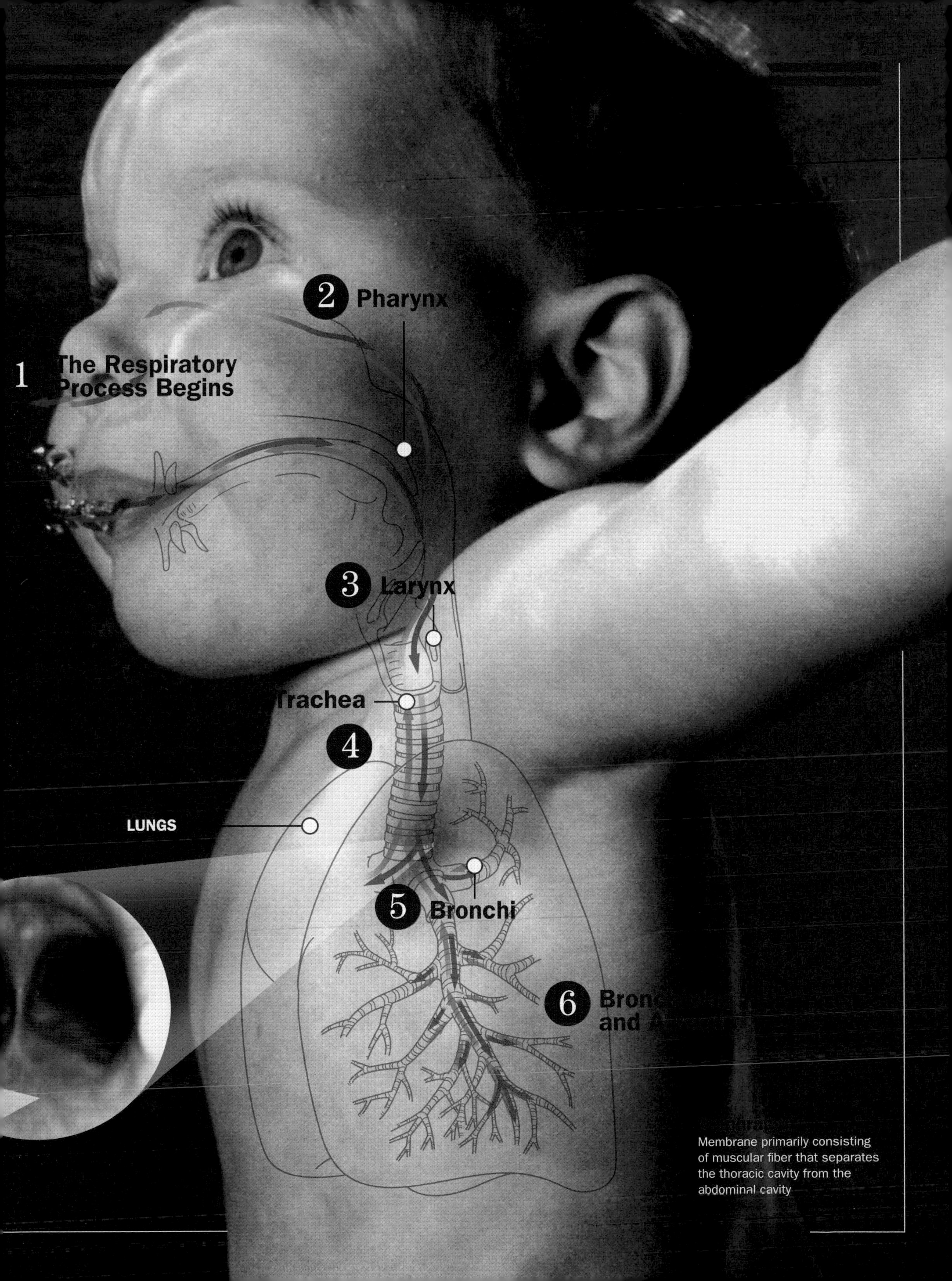

1 **The Respiratory Process Begins**

2 **Pharynx**

3 **Larynx**

Trachea

4

LUNGS

5 **Bronchi**

6 **Bron** **and A**

Membrane primarily consisting
of muscular fiber that separates
the thoracic cavity from the
abdominal cavity

Digestive System

The digestive system transforms food into fuel for the entire body. The process begins with ingestion through the mouth and esophagus and continues with digestion in the stomach, the small intestine, and the large intestine, from which the feces are evacuated by the rectum and anus. Separating the useful from the useless requires the filtering of the kidneys, which discard the waste in urine.

Peristalsis: Muscles in Action

Peristalsis is the group of muscular actions that moves the food toward the stomach.

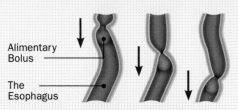

Alimentary Bolus

The Esophagus

Food is sent toward the stomach.

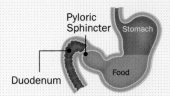

Pyloric Sphincter
Stomach
Duodenum
Food

Full stomach

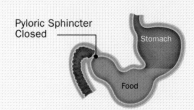

Pyloric Sphincter Closed
Stomach
Food

The stomach in full digestive action

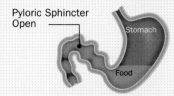

Pyloric Sphincter Open
Stomach
Food

The stomach is being emptied.

The First Step: Ingestion

The digestive process begins with the mouth.

THE SOFT PALATE

THE HARD PALATE

TONGUE

PHARYNX

ESOPHAGUS

10 inches (25 cm)
IS THE LENGTH OF THE ESOPHAGUS.

Digestion Chronology

① **00:00:00**
Food reaches the mouth.

② **00:00:10**
The food is transformed into a moist alimentary bolus.

③ **03:00:00**
The food leaves the stomach.

④ **06:00:00**
The food arrives at the midpoint of the small intestine.

⑤ **08:00:00**
The non-digested, watery residue arrives at the junction of the small and large intestines.

20:00:00
The alimentary residue remains in the large intestine between 12 and 28 hours.

⑥ **24:00**
Between 20 and 44 hours after having entered the mouth as food, the residue arrives at the rectum.

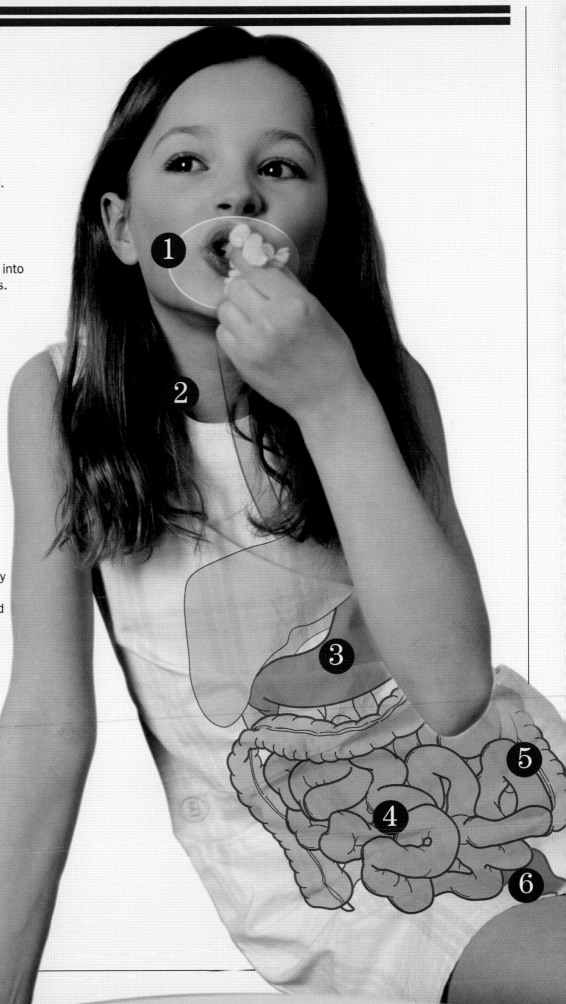

Liver, Pancreas, Bile

The liver is the largest gland of the human body. It produces bile, a yellowish-green fluid that helps in the digestion of fats. The liver is the great regulator of the glucose level of the blood, which it stores in the form of glycogen. Glycogen can be released when the organism requires more sugar for activity. The liver regulates the *metabolism* of *proteins*. The liver is also a large blood filter and a storage site for vitamins A, D, E, and K. The pancreas is a gland that assists in digestion, secreting pancreatic juice.

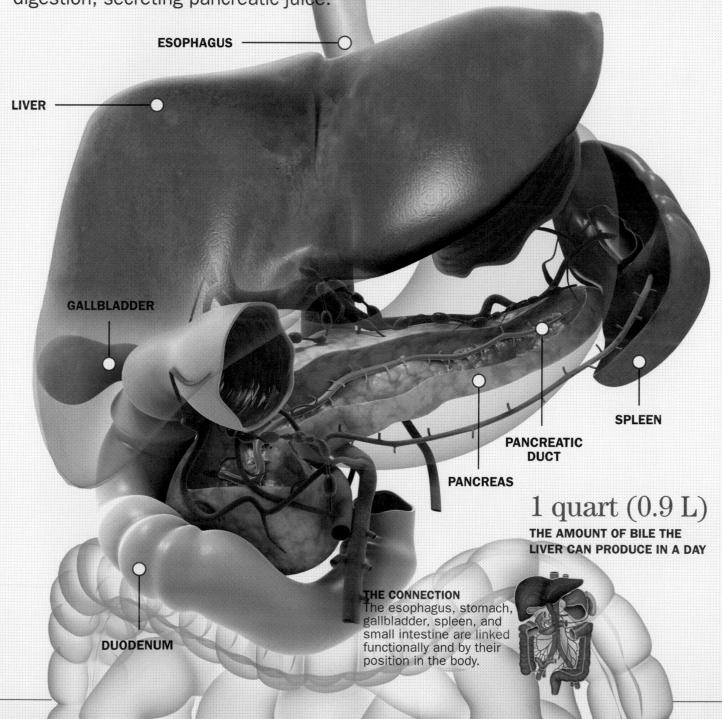

ESOPHAGUS

LIVER

GALLBLADDER

SPLEEN

PANCREATIC DUCT

PANCREAS

DUODENUM

1 quart (0.9 L)
THE AMOUNT OF BILE THE LIVER CAN PRODUCE IN A DAY

THE CONNECTION
The esophagus, stomach, gallbladder, spleen, and small intestine are linked functionally and by their position in the body.

Large and Small Intestine

The intestines are the longest part of the digestive tract. The small intestine receives the food from the stomach. Digestion continues through enzyme activity, which completes the chemical breakdown of the food. The walls of the small intestine absorb the nutrients derived from the chemical transformation of the food. The nutrients then pass into the bloodstream. Waste substances will go to the large intestine. There the final stage of the digestive process will occur: the formation of the feces to be excreted.

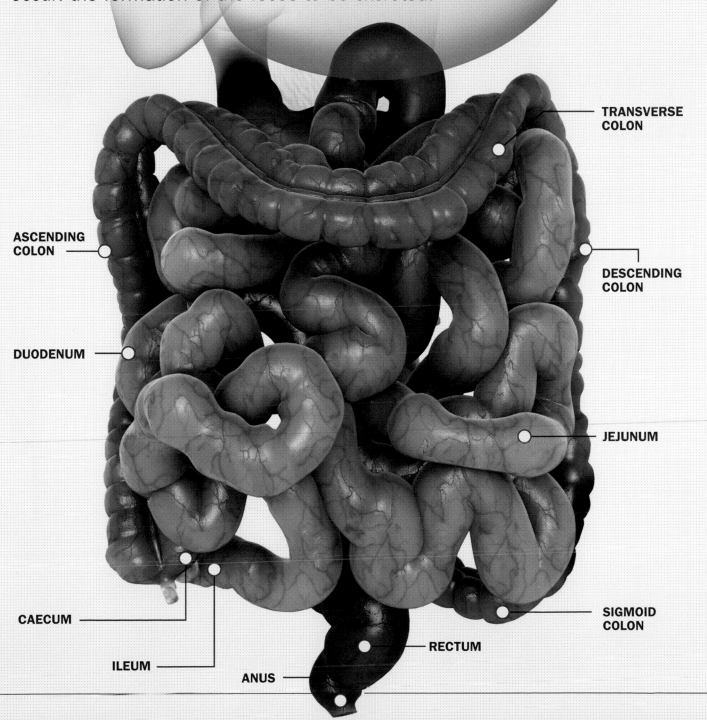

TRANSVERSE COLON

ASCENDING COLON

DESCENDING COLON

DUODENUM

JEJUNUM

CAECUM

SIGMOID COLON

ILEUM

RECTUM

ANUS

Urinary System

Its basic organs are the kidneys (2), the ureters (2), the bladder, and the urethra. Its function is to regulate homeostasis, maintaining the equilibrium between the water and the chemicals in the body. The first phase of this objective is accomplished when the kidneys produce and secrete urine, a liquid that is eliminated from the body. The ureters are channels that carry the urine through the body. The bladder is a sac that stores the urine until it is passed to the urethra, a duct through which it will be expelled from the body.

COMPONENTS OF URINE

95%	**Water**
2%	**Urea**, a toxic substance
2%	**Chloride salts**, sulfates, phosphates of potassium and magnesium
1%	**Uric acid**

The Bladder in Action

The bladder is continually filled with urine and then emptied periodically. When full, the bladder stretches to increase its capacity.

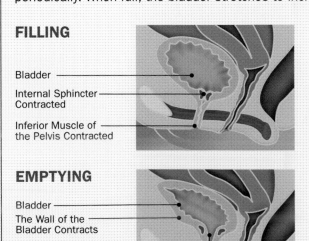

FILLING

Bladder
Internal Sphincter Contracted
Inferior Muscle of the Pelvis Contracted

EMPTYING

Bladder
The Wall of the Bladder Contracts
Internal Sphincter Relaxed
Inferior Muscle of the Pelvis Relaxed

41 to 51
fluid ounces
(1,200 to 1,500 cc)

IS THE AMOUNT OF URINE ELIMINATED EACH DAY BY AN ADULT.

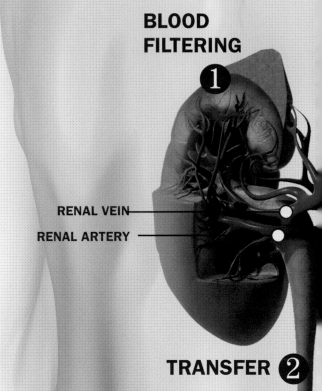

BLOOD FILTERING 1

RENAL VEIN
RENAL ARTERY

TRANSFER 2

ABDOMINAL AORTA

STORAGE 3

BLADDER

ELIMINATION 4

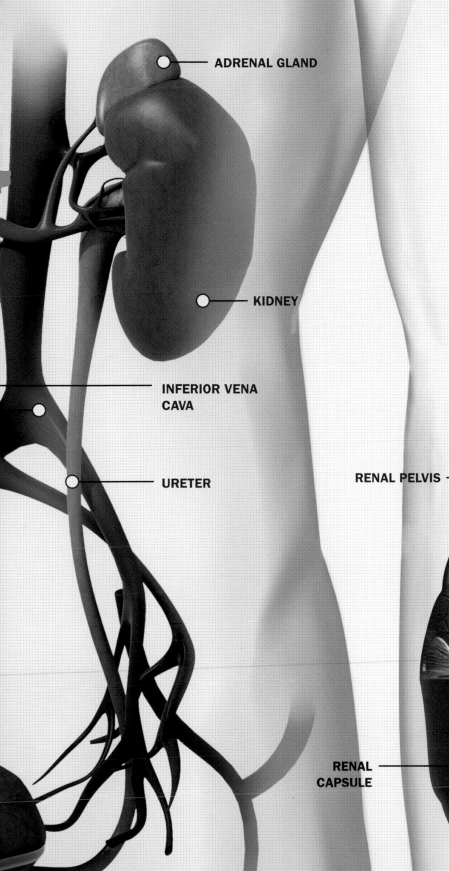

ADRENAL GLAND

KIDNEY

INFERIOR VENA CAVA

URETER

The Renal Circuit

1. Entry of Blood
2. Filtration
3. Urine Is Obtained
4. Urine
5. Clean Blood

RENAL PYRAMID

RENAL VEIN

RENAL PELVIS

❷

❸

❺

RENAL CAPSULE

❶

❹

RENAL ARTERY

URETER

Endocrine System

It consists of the glands inside the body that secrete approximately 50 specific substances called hormones into the blood. The hormones activate or stimulate various organs and control reproduction, development, and metabolism. These chemicals control many of the body's processes and even meddle in our love lives.

The Hormonal Message

The endocrine system is made up of the endocrine glands. This complex, controlled by the pituitary (hypophysis), or master, gland, includes the thyroid, parathyroid, pancreas, ovaries, testicles, adrenals, pineal, and hypothalamus.

Pituitary Hormones

ACTH Adrenocorticotropin hormone

TSH A hormone that stimulates the thyroid

GH Growth hormone

FSH Follicle-stimulating hormone

LH Luteinizing hormone

MSH Hormone that stimulates the melanocyte of the skin

ADH Antidiuretic hormone

PRL Prolactin

OXYTOCIN

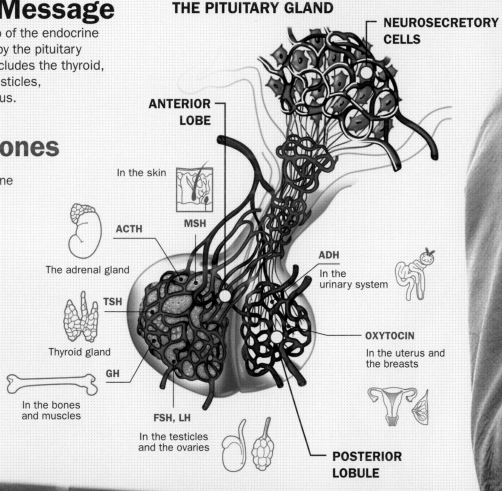

THE PITUITARY GLAND

NEUROSECRETORY CELLS

ANTERIOR LOBE

In the skin

ACTH

MSH

ADH

In the urinary system

The adrenal gland

TSH

Thyroid gland

GH

OXYTOCIN

In the uterus and the breasts

In the bones and muscles

FSH, LH

In the testicles and the ovaries

POSTERIOR LOBULE

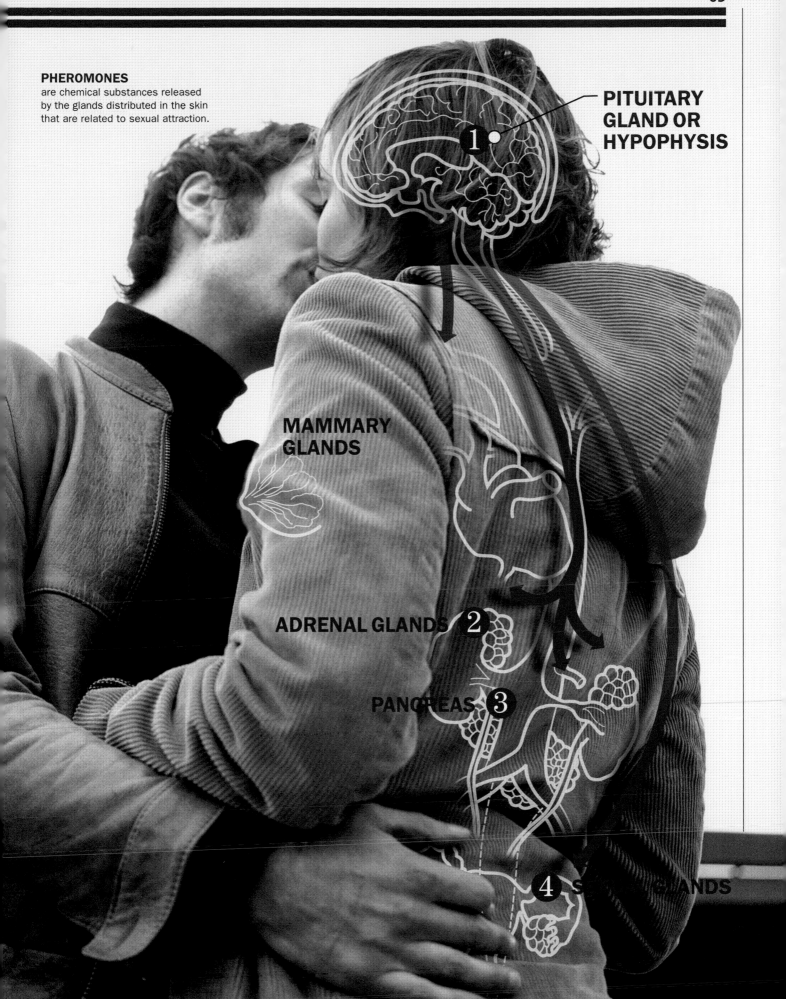

PHEROMONES
are chemical substances released by the glands distributed in the skin that are related to sexual attraction.

PITUITARY GLAND OR HYPOPHYSIS

1

MAMMARY GLANDS

ADRENAL GLANDS 2

PANCREAS 3

4 S   GLANDS

Reproduction and Pregnancy

The male reproductive system is the complex of organs that leads to a man's production of one of two types of cells necessary for the creation of a new being. The female reproductive system produces ova, and its organs are arranged so as to allow the fertilization of the ovum by a spermatozoon of the male reproductive system. Fertilization is the starting point for the development of pregnancy. The sperm and the egg fuse together, giving rise to a zygote. Human pregnancies last nine months.

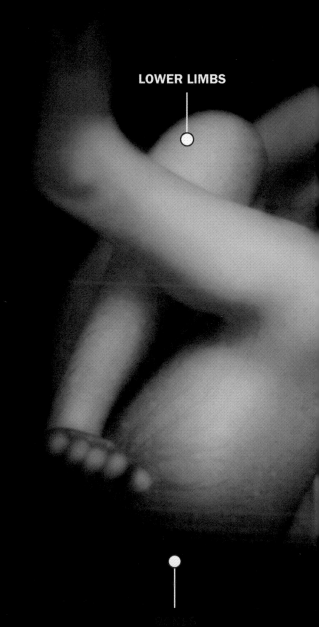

LOWER LIMBS

160
IS THE NUMBER OF HEARTBEATS PER MINUTE IN THE EARLY STAGES OF INTRAUTERINE LIFE.

MILESTONES

TIME	DEVELOPMENT
	The embryo's heart begins to beat.
	The lungs and brain begin to develop.
	The taste buds develop.
	The spinal cord develops.
	Toenails become visible
	The fetus can suck its thumb.
	The fetus begins to blink.

A fetus has
300 bones.
AFTER BIRTH AND BEFORE ADULTHOOD, THE SKELETAL SYSTEM GOES THROUGH A FUSION PROCESS THAT REDUCES THE NUMBER OF BONES TO 206.

Month
4

LENGTH: 5.9 INCHES (15 CM)
WEIGHT: 5.3 OUNCES (150 G)

100 billion neurons
**ARE FORMED BETWEEN THE THIRD AND
SEVENTH MONTHS OF FETAL DEVELOPMENT.**

⦿———— FINGERS

⦿————

Right
Atrium

Superior
Vena Cava

Foramen
Ovale

Aorta

Right
Ventricle

Left
Atrium

Left
Ventricle

The Heart

Circulatory System
The fetus receives oxygen and nutrients from
the placenta through the umbilical cord.

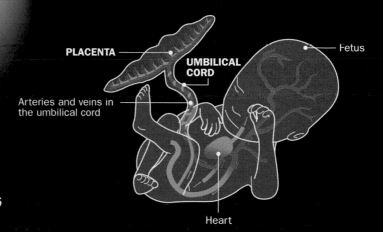

PLACENTA ————

———— Fetus

UMBILICAL
CORD

Arteries and veins in
the umbilical cord ————

Heart

SKIN

UPPER LIMBS

4-D Ultrasound

The 4-D ultrasound is the latest word in diagnostic examinations in *obstetrics*. It produces color images in real time that give the impression of watching a movie of a baby as it is growing inside the uterus. However, it is not a movie properly speaking but the sweep of ultrasonic waves that are reflected as echoes by the fetus.

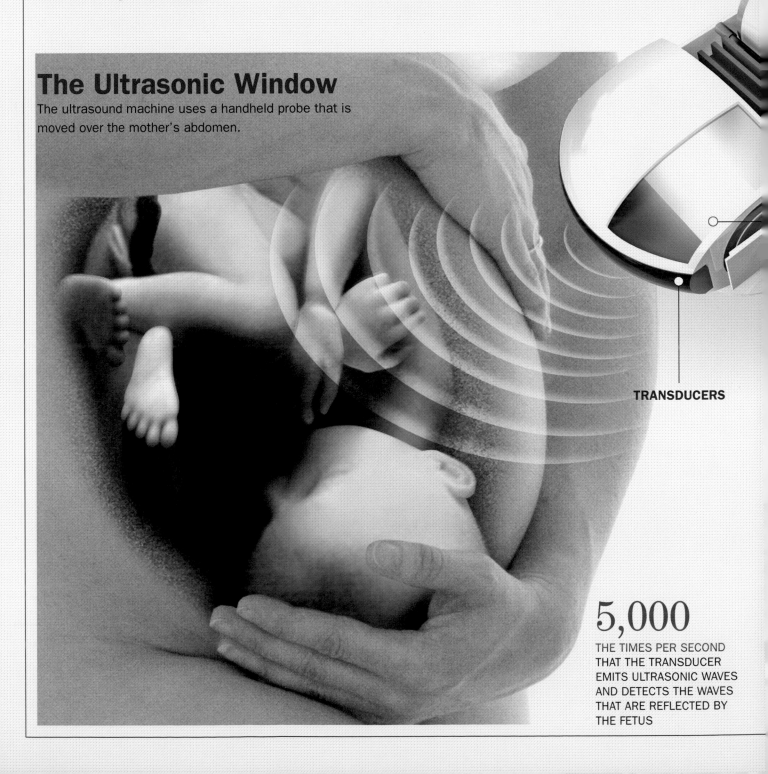

The Ultrasonic Window

The ultrasound machine uses a handheld probe that is moved over the mother's abdomen.

TRANSDUCERS

5,000

THE TIMES PER SECOND THAT THE TRANSDUCER EMITS ULTRASONIC WAVES AND DETECTS THE WAVES THAT ARE REFLECTED BY THE FETUS

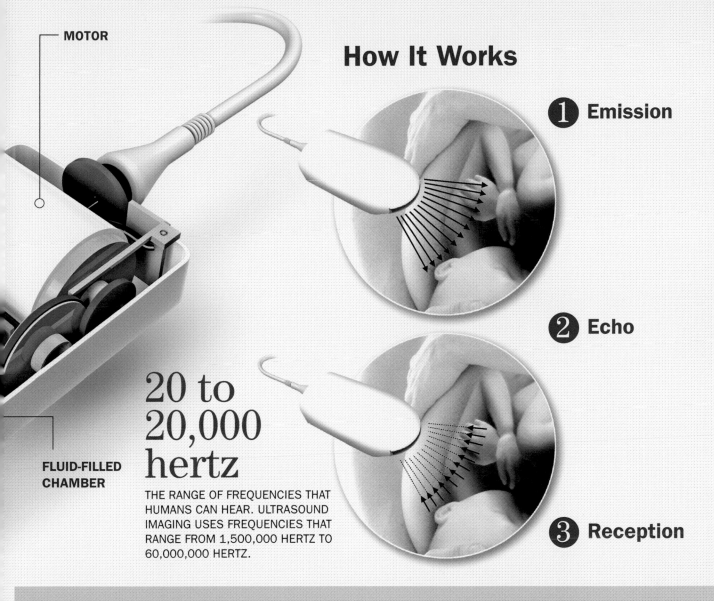

MOTOR

FLUID-FILLED
CHAMBER

How It Works

① **Emission**

② **Echo**

③ **Reception**

20 to 20,000 hertz

THE RANGE OF FREQUENCIES THAT
HUMANS CAN HEAR. ULTRASOUND
IMAGING USES FREQUENCIES THAT
RANGE FROM 1,500,000 HERTZ TO
60,000,000 HERTZ.

Development

Ultrasound imaging technology has developed in recent
years from producing somewhat confusing multicolored
pictures to movielike images of the fetus in the uterus.

2-D ULTRASOUND

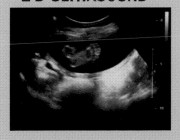

3-D ULTRASOUND

4-D ULTRASOUND

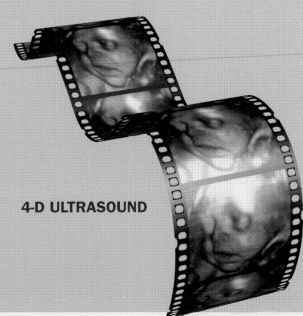

Nervous System

The nervous system is the body's most complex system, many of whose characteristics and potentialities are still unknown. Together with the endocrine system, the brain has the job of controlling the organism. Its specific functions are rapid and intellectual activities, such as memory, emotions, and will. The nervous system is divided into two portions: the central (the brain and the spinal cord) and the peripheral (nerves of the cranium and the rest of the body). The cells that make up the nervous system are called neurons. They transmit images in the form of electric signals.

The Great Coordinator

The nervous system acts as the great coordinator of the functions of all the parts and organs of the body.

0.001

WHEN A FIBER TRANSMITS A NERVE IMPULSE, A CERTAIN AMOUNT OF TIME IS NEEDED BEFORE IT CAN TRANSMIT THE NEXT IMPULSE. THIS "REST" LASTS BETWEEN 0.001 AND 0.005 SECONDS.

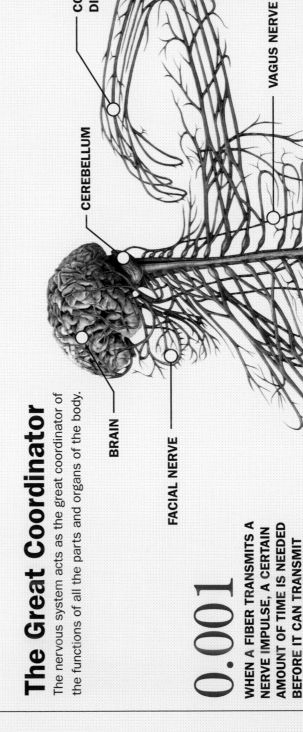

CEREBELLUM

COMMON PALMAR DIGITAL NERVE

BRAIN

FACIAL NERVE

VAGUS NERVE

SPINAL CORD

LUMBAR PLEXUS

MEDIAL NERVE

Central

Consists of the brain (cerebrum, cerebellum, and spinal bulb) and the spinal column.

Peripheral

Its functions are to provide information to the central nervous system and to coordinate movements.

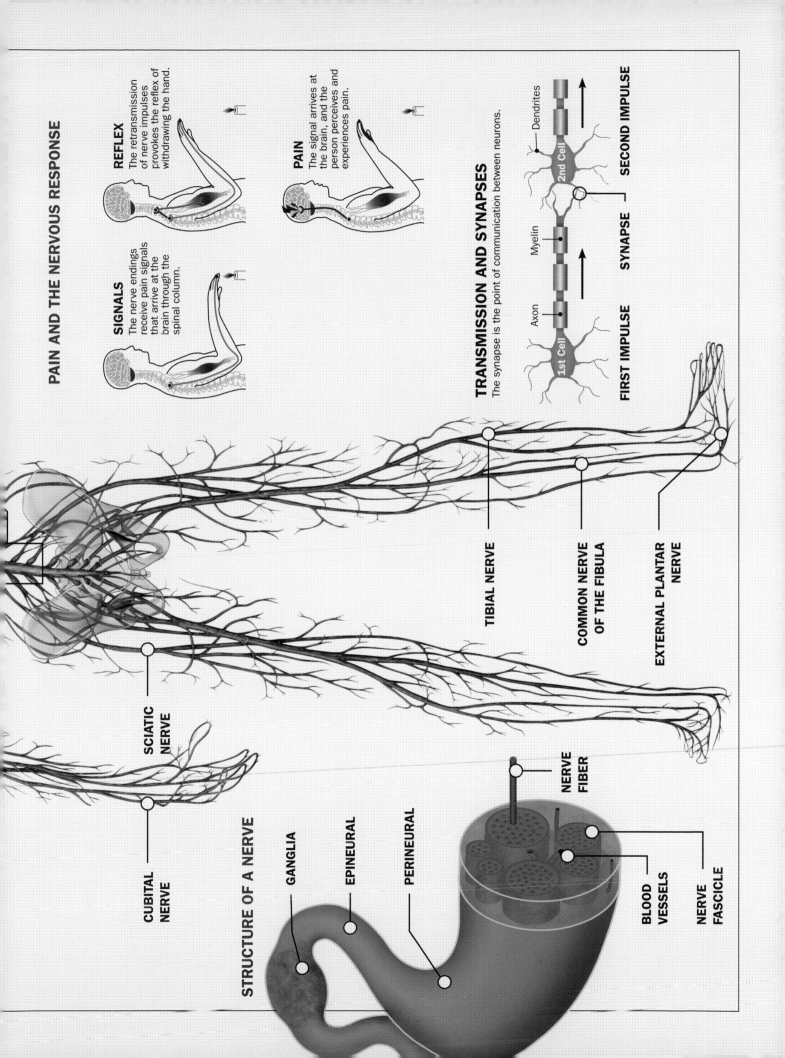

PAIN AND THE NERVOUS RESPONSE

SIGNALS
The nerve endings receive pain signals that arrive at the brain through the spinal column.

REFLEX
The retransmission of nerve impulses provokes the reflex of withdrawing the hand.

PAIN
The signal arrives at the brain, and the person perceives and experiences pain.

TRANSMISSION AND SYNAPSES
The synapse is the point of communication between neurons.

1st Cell

Axon

Myelin

2nd Cell

Dendrites

FIRST IMPULSE   SYNAPSE   SECOND IMPULSE

TIBIAL NERVE

COMMON NERVE OF THE FIBULA

EXTERNAL PLANTAR NERVE

SCIATIC NERVE

CUBITAL NERVE

STRUCTURE OF A NERVE

GANGLIA

EPINEURAL

PERINEURAL

NERVE FIBER

BLOOD VESSELS

NERVE FASCICLE

The Brain

The brain is the body's control center. Underneath its folds more than 100 billion neurons organize and examine incoming information and act as a guide for the organism. In spite of amounting to only 2 percent of the total weight of a human body, the brain alone uses one fifth of the oxygen inhaled. It is one of the most fragile parts of the body and, therefore, one of the most protected.

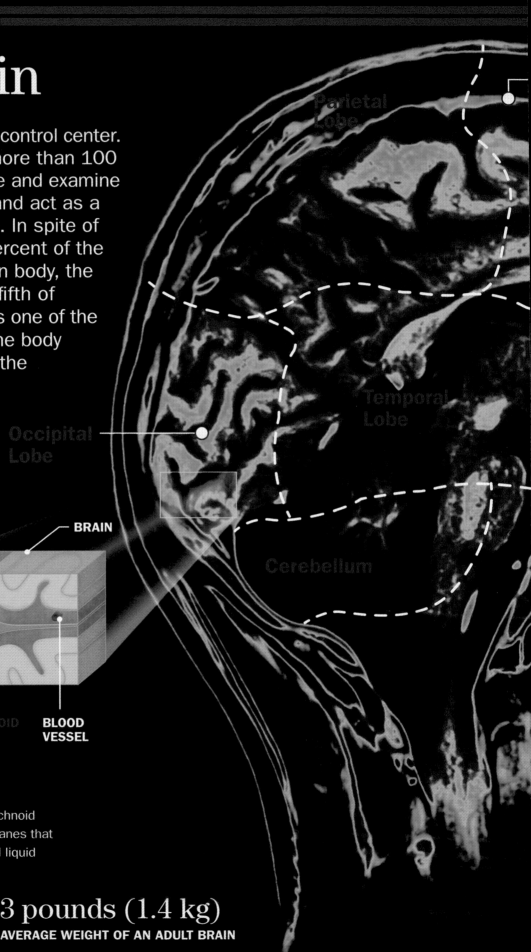

Parietal Lobe

Occipital Lobe

Temporal Lobe

Cerebellum

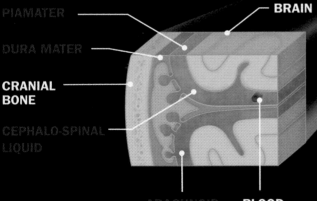

MENINGES

PIAMATER

DURA MATER

CRANIAL BONE

CEPHALO-SPINAL LIQUID

— **BRAIN**

ARACHNOID

BLOOD VESSEL

Meninges

The dura mater, piamater, and arachnoid are the three meninges, or membranes that cover the brain. The cephalo-spinal liquid circulates within the meninges.

3 pounds (1.4 kg)
AVERAGE WEIGHT OF AN ADULT BRAIN

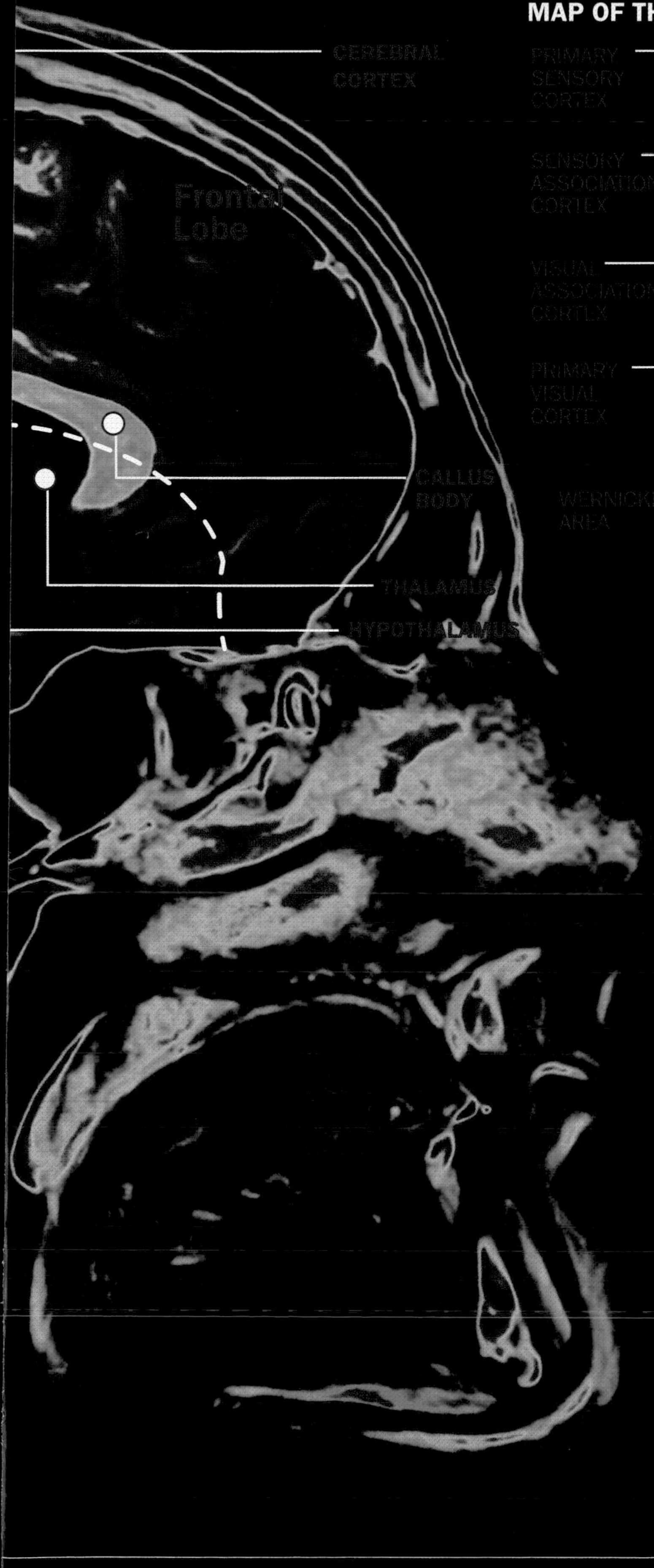

MAP OF THE BRAIN

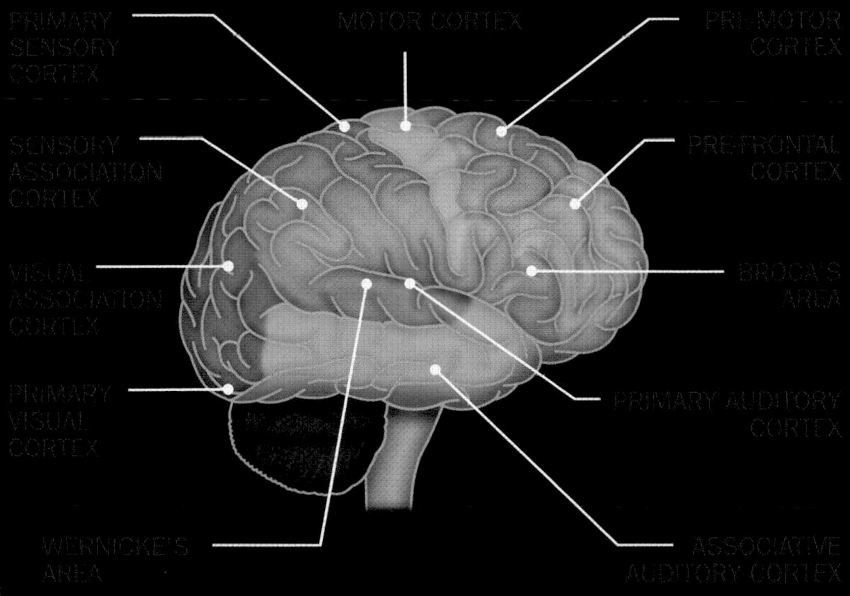

CEREBRAL CORTEX

PRIMARY SENSORY CORTEX

MOTOR CORTEX

PRE-MOTOR CORTEX

Frontal Lobe

SENSORY ASSOCIATION CORTEX

PRE-FRONTAL CORTEX

VISUAL ASSOCIATION CORTEX

BROCA'S AREA

PRIMARY VISUAL CORTEX

PRIMARY AUDITORY CORTEX

CALLUS BODY

WERNICKE'S AREA

ASSOCIATIVE AUDITORY CORTEX

THALAMUS

HYPOTHALAMUS

Spinal Medulla

The spinal medulla is the spinal cord, which goes from the cephalic trunk to the lumbar region. Together with the brain it forms the central nervous system.

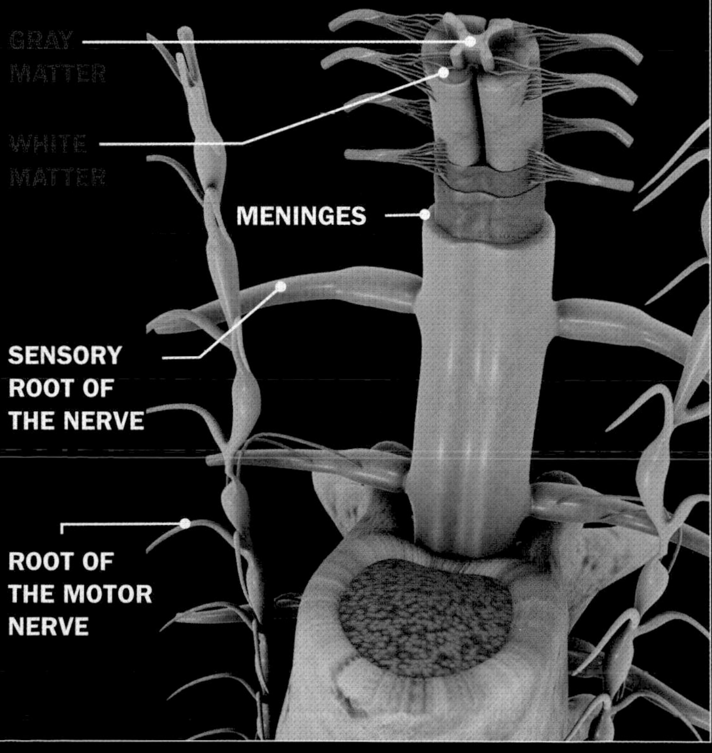

GRAY MATTER

WHITE MATTER

MENINGES

SENSORY ROOT OF THE NERVE

ROOT OF THE MOTOR NERVE

Smell and Taste

These two senses function as powerful allies of the digestive system. Taste involves the perception of dissolved chemical substances arriving, for example, in the form of food. Taste sensation is principally seated on the upper surface of the tongue, and *saliva* is a fundamental ingredient for dissolving and tasting. Smell involves the perception of these chemicals when they take the form of dispersed aromas. The sense of smell operates at a greater distance than that of taste and can capture substances floating in the environment.

Olfactory Cells

These are located deep in the nasal cavity, extended over the olfactory epithelium. It is calculated that some 25 million cells are located there.

10,000

THE NUMBER OF ODORS THE SENSE OF SMELL CAN DISTINGUISH

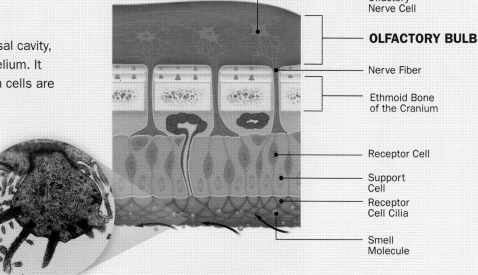

Olfactory Nerve Cell

OLFACTORY BULB

Nerve Fiber

Ethmoid Bone of the Cranium

Receptor Cell

Support Cell

Receptor Cell Cilia

Smell Molecule

Gustatory Papillae

The tongue is the principal seat of the sense of taste. It has great mobility at the bottom of the mouth and contains between 5,000 and 12,000 gustatory papillae.

GUSTATORY PAPILLA

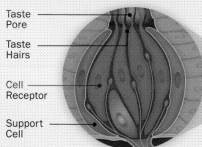

Taste Pore

Taste Hairs

Cell Receptor

Support Cell

SURFACE OF THE TONGUE

4 Flavors

THE SURFACE OF THE TONGUE CAN DISTINGUISH: SWEET, SALTY, SOUR, AND BITTER.

Touch and the Skin

Touch is one of the five senses. Its function is to perceive sensations of contact, pressure, and temperature and to send them to the brain. It is located in the skin, the organ that covers the entire outside of the body for protection. When the skin records external changes (of temperature, for example), it activates reflexive mechanisms to open or close the pores and, thus, to maintain the required body temperature. Secretions, such as those of the sweat glands, also contribute to this process by reducing heat.

The Thinnest and the Thickest

The thinnest skin on the body is that of the eyelids. The thickest is that of the sole of the foot.

RESPONDING TO TEMPERATURE

When the skin perceives the sensation of cold, the blood vessels and the muscles contract. The purpose of this is to prevent the escape of heat. The opposite happens in response to the heat.

MERKEL DISK
Detects pressure

UPPER SQUAMOUS LAYER

EPIDERMIS

DERMIS

SUBCUTANEOUS FAT

Hair Standing On End

Goose Bumps

Contracted Vessel

Contracted Muscle

Dilated Vessel

Perspiration

MEISSNER CORPUSCLES
Their task is to detect fine touch.

Anatomy of the Eye

The eye, one of the most complex organs of the body, allows us to judge the size and texture of an object even before we touch it or to know how far away it is. More than 100 million cells are activated instantaneously in the presence of light, converting the image perceived into nerve impulses that are transmitted to the brain. 70 percent of all the body's sensory receptors are concentrated in the eyes.

How Does the Eye See?

An object reflects light in all directions. The light is partially focused by the cornea. The lens changes its shape to give the light the focus it needs. The rays cross the inside of the eye. The light arrives at the retina, and the rays perceived produce an inverted image of the object. The retina sends this information to the brain, which processes it and constructs a correct image of the object.

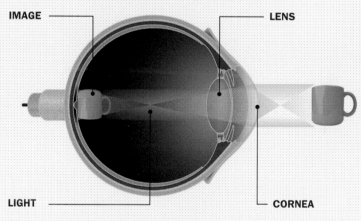

IMAGE
LENS
LIGHT
CORNEA

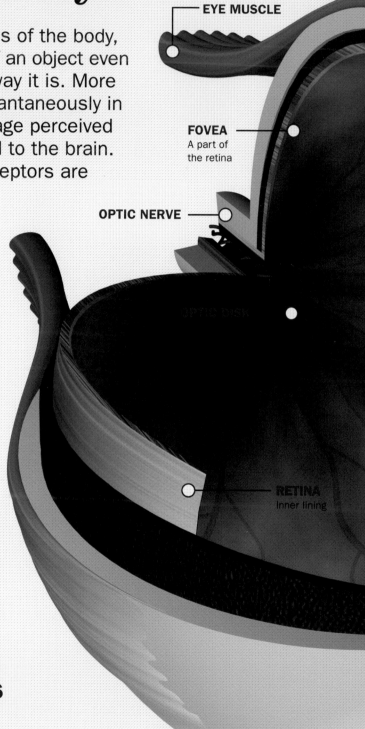

EYE MUSCLE

FOVEA
A part of the retina

OPTIC NERVE

RETINA
Inner lining

Seeing in Three Dimensions

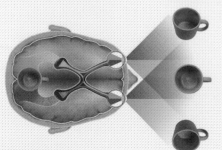

IMAGE 1
The left eye's perception

IMAGE 2
The images from both eyes come together

IMAGE 3
The right eye's perception

Rods and Cones

There are two types of photosensitive cells that transform light into electrical impulses. The rods function to "see" only in black and white. The cones see colors in detail.

SCLERA
A hard, opaque, and whitish membrane

CILIARY BODY
Contains muscles

LENS
A disk that focuses light

CORNEA
Hard and transparent membrane

EYELASH

PUPIL

IRIS

EYELID

VISION PROBLEMS

Retina

A HYPEROPIA (FARSIGHTEDNESS)

Retina

B MYOPIA (NEARSIGHTEDNESS)

C COLOR BLINDNESS

Protection

EYEBROWS

EYELASH

LACHRYMAL GLAND

Mechanics of Hearing

The ear is responsible for hearing and maintaining equilibrium. When the ear perceives sounds, it registers its characteristics—volume, tone, and timbre—as well as the direction from which it comes. The ear is capable of distinguishing a great range of volumes, from the buzzing of a mosquito to the roar of an airplane. A group of nerve terminals receives information about the body's motion and transmits this to the brain in order to maintain dynamic and static equilibrium.

Frequencies

The frequency of a sound is the speed at which the sound makes the air vibrate.

FREQUENCIES AUDIBLE TO HUMANS AND ANIMALS

SUBJECT	MINIMUM	MAXIMUM
Person 10 years old	20 Hz	20,000 Hz
Person 60 years old	20 Hz	12,000 Hz
Dog	60 Hz	45,000 Hz
Frog	100 Hz	3,000 Hz
Bat	1,000 Hz	120,000 Hz
Cat	60 Hz	65,000 Hz

Organ of Corti

Contains ciliary cells that collect vibrations.

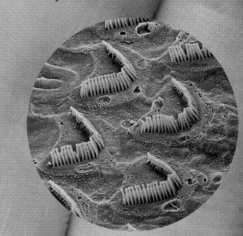

THE PROCESSING OF SOUND

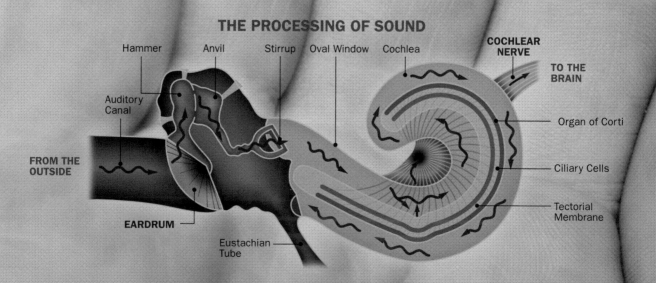

Hammer
Anvil
Stirrup
Oval Window
Cochlea
COCHLEAR NERVE
TO THE BRAIN
Auditory Canal
Organ of Corti
FROM THE OUTSIDE
Ciliary Cells
EARDRUM
Tectorial Membrane
Eustachian Tube

1 ENTRANCE **2** VIBRATION **3** TRANSMISSION TO THE BRAIN

Dynamic and static equilibrium are maintained by the inner ear. Above the cochlea there are three semicircular canals, which are spiral-shaped conduits. Inside the canals are a gelatinous membrane and thousands of *cilia*, traversed by a cranial nerve that connects them to the brain. When the head moves, this gelatinous membrane is displaced, and the tiny cilia send the brain information about the velocity and the direction of this displacement.

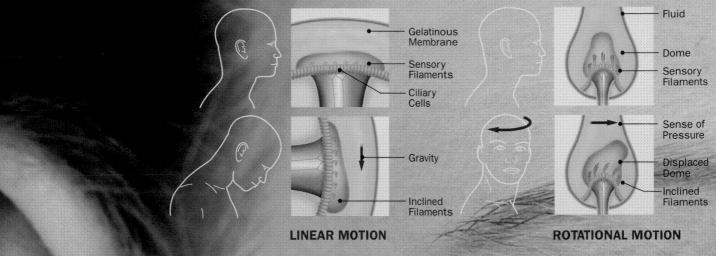

Gelatinous Membrane

Sensory Filaments

Ciliary Cells

Gravity

Inclined Filaments

LINEAR MOTION

Fluid

Dome

Sensory Filaments

Sense of Pressure

Displaced Dome

Inclined Filaments

ROTATIONAL MOTION

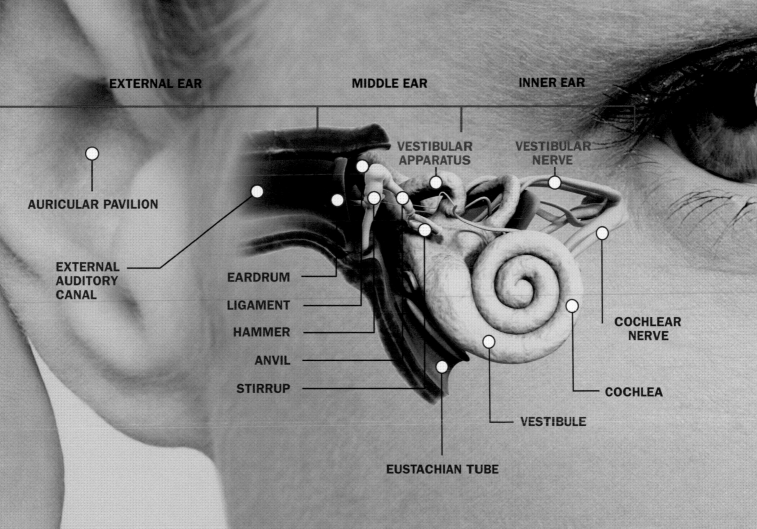

EXTERNAL EAR

MIDDLE EAR

INNER EAR

VESTIBULAR APPARATUS

VESTIBULAR NERVE

AURICULAR PAVILION

EXTERNAL AUDITORY CANAL

EARDRUM

LIGAMENT

HAMMER

ANVIL

STIRRUP

COCHLEAR NERVE

COCHLEA

VESTIBULE

EUSTACHIAN TUBE

Early Diagnosis

There are various methods of examining the body to search for possible diseases.

X-Rays

The simple emission of X-rays consists of sending out short electromagnetic waves. After passing through the body, they reach a photographic film and create shadow images.

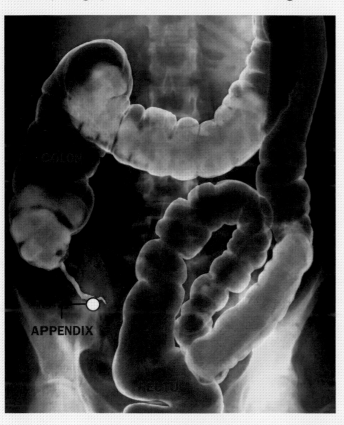

APPENDIX

SPINAL
CORD

UMBILICAL
CORD

**3-D MAGNETIC ▶
RESONANCE IMAGING**

ULTRASOUND ▼
The ultrasound uses high frequency sound waves.

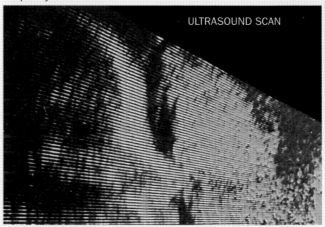

ULTRASOUND SCAN

**◀ POSITRON EMISSION
TOMOGRAPHY**

**METABOLIC
ACTIVITY**

1 inch (3 CM

Miniature
Camera

ENCAPSULATED CAMERA ▲
A miniature camera enters the body.

Magnetic
Field

**MAGNETIC ▶
RESONANCE
IMAGING**

WALLS
contain a very strong magnetic cylinder